Grade 5

Benchmark Assessment

Mc Graw Hill **Education**

Bothell, WA • Chicago, IL • Columbus, OH • New York, NY

www.mheonline.com/readingwonders

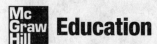 **Education**

Copyright © by The McGraw-Hill Companies, Inc.

All rights reserved. The contents, or parts thereof, may be
reproduced in print form for non-profit educational use with
McGraw-Hill Reading Wonders provided such reproductions
bear copyright notice, but may not be reproduced in any form
for any other purpose without the prior written consent of The
McGraw-Hill Companies, Inc., including, but not limited to,
network storage or transmission, or broadcast for distance
learning.

Send all inquiries to:
McGraw-Hill Education
Two Penn Plaza
New York, New York 10121

Printed in the United States of America

4 5 6 7 8 9 QMD 17 16 15 14 13
C

The **McGraw·Hill** Companies

Table of Contents

Copyright © The McGraw-Hill Companies, Inc.

Benchmark Assessment

Benchmark Assessment is an integral part of the complete assessment program aligned with *McGraw-Hill Reading Wonders* and the Common Core State Standards (CCSS).

Purpose of *Benchmark Assessment*

Benchmark Assessment reports on the outcome of student learning and provides a status of current achievement in relation to the CCSS-aligned curriculum. The results of the assessments can be used to inform subsequent instruction, aid in making leveling and grouping decisions, and point toward areas in need of reteaching or remediation.

Benchmark Assessment tests are constructed to mirror the approach, administration, and subject concentration found in criterion-referenced testing. Performance in these assessments can act as a signal of student readiness for the demands of high-stakes testing as well as a snapshot of student progress toward end-of-year goals.

Focus of *Benchmark Assessment*

Benchmark Assessment focuses on the following key areas of English Language Arts as identified by the CCSS:

- Comprehension of literature
- Comprehension of informational text
- Using text features to access or clarify information
- Vocabulary acquisition and use
- Command of the conventions of standard English language
- Writing within the parameters of specific text types

Copyright © The McGraw-Hill Companies, Inc.

Teacher Introduction

Overview of *Benchmark Assessment*

Benchmark Assessment consists of two tests—Benchmark 1 and Benchmark 2.

Benchmark 1 focuses on skills from Units 1, 2, and 3; Benchmark 2 samples skills from the entire year. Each test is in two parts—Part 1: Reading and Part 2: Writing.

Part 1: Reading

In this section of the test, students read a variety of literature and informational "Cold Read" texts on which **60** multiple-choice items are based. These items assess student understanding of the text through the use of Comprehension Skills, Literary Elements, and Text Features and students' ability to uncover the meanings of unknown and multiple-meaning words and phrases using Vocabulary Strategies.

Part 2: Writing

In this section of the test, students read drafts of written work, cloze passages, and writing plans on which **50** multiple-choice items are based. Students demonstrate their command of the conventions of standard English language and their understanding of the writing process as they correct errors, clarify writing by editing/revising, and improve existing drafts/writing plans.

After students complete the multiple-choice section of Part 2, they craft a written response to a prompt in a previously-taught text type. This activity assesses students' ability to write on demand in response to a prompt and is consistent with the writing performance students encounter in high-stakes testing. Students use the lines provided to plan their writing and compose their final version on a separate sheet of paper.

Administering *Benchmark Assessment*

Benchmark 1 should be given to students after Unit 3 is completed. Benchmark 2 should be given to students close to the end of the year or before students take their high-stakes state test.

Due to the length of the test (and to provide students a test-taking experience that is in concert with standardized testing), the schedule below is suggested. Sessions can be spaced over a number of days or grouped together with short breaks in between.

- Session 1—Complete half (or approximately half) of Part 1: Reading (60 to 70 minutes)
- Session 2—Finish Part 1: Reading (60 to 70 minutes)
- Session 3—Complete the multiple-choice portion of Part 2: Writing (55 to 65 minutes)
- Session 4—Respond to the prompt in Part 2: Writing (40 to 50 minutes)

Remind students of the following key information as they prepare to begin a session:

- *Write your name and the date on the question pages for this assessment.*
- *Read each selection and question carefully.*
- *For multiple-choice items, completely fill in the circle next to the correct answer.*
- *For the writing prompt, plan your writing on the lines provided and craft your final version on another sheet of paper.*
- *You have [provide time limit] to complete this part of the assessment. You may begin now.*

Answer procedural questions during the assessment, but do not provide any assistance on the items or selections. Have extra paper on hand for students to use for their responses to the prompt. After the class has completed the assessment, ask students to verify that their names and the date are written on the necessary pages.

Copyright © The McGraw-Hill Companies, Inc.

Benchmark Assessment Reporting Categories

To assist with identifying literacy areas in need of improvement, the items in **Benchmark Assessment** are aligned with distinct categories.

Reading Category 1—Vocabulary

Items in this category assess students' ability to use vocabulary strategies to uncover the meanings of words and phrases. This category focuses on context clues, word parts (root/base words and affixes), words with multiple meanings, connotation and denotation, antonyms, and synonyms. The items in this category comprise approximately 20% of Part 1: Reading.

Reading Categories 2 and 3—Comprehension and Analysis of Text

Items in these categories assess students' ability to use comprehension skills to access meaning from text and to analyze elements of text. These categories focus on main ideas and key details, recognizing an author's view/claims, acknowledging text structures, comparing and contrasting within and between texts, finding cause-and-effect relationships, character point of view, the author's use of figurative language, identifying theme, and character, plot, and setting. The items in these categories comprise approximately 70% of Part 1: Reading.

Reading Category 4—Text Features

Items in this category assess students' ability to recognize how authors employ text features to aid in comprehension of the text and to provide organizational markers. The items in this category comprise approximately 10% of Part 1: Reading.

Writing Categories

The main differentiator in Part 2: Writing is between the multiple-choice items and the written response to the prompt. When a writing plan is featured, the multiple-choice items are separated into Prewriting/Organization and English Language Conventions strands.

Scoring Benchmark Assessment

Each multiple-choice item is worth one point, and the prompt is worth four points.

To clearly monitor progress, you can view each Benchmark as three individual scores: the Reading score, the Writing multiple-choice score, and the Writing Prompt score.

Copyright © The McGraw-Hill Companies, Inc.

Teacher Introduction

Scoring *Benchmark Assessment*

The Writing Prompt should be scored using the rubric found below.

4-Point Scoring Rubric

	Focus	Organization	Support	Conventions
4	Consistent focus is maintained throughout the writing.	Writing employs an appropriate organizational strategy that is followed throughout.	Writing is clearly supported by specific details. The word choice is precise and engaging.	Writing contains few, if any, errors in the conventions of standard English.
3	Consistent focus is maintained for the most part.	Writing employs an organizational strategy, with occasional digressions.	Writing has supporting details and the word choice serves the purpose of the writing but is not very precise.	Writing contains some errors in the conventions of standard English.
2	Writing loses focus at times.	Writing attempts to use an organizational strategy but it is not clear or consistent.	Writing has few supporting details and the word choice is often simple or unclear.	Writing contains several errors in the conventions of standard English.
1	Writing does not have a consistent focus.	Writing has no organizational strategy.	Writing has a lack of supporting details and the word choice is limited.	Writing contains serious errors in the conventions of standard English.

Unscorable responses are unrelated to the topic, illegible, or contain little or no writing.

Copyright © The McGraw-Hill Companies, Inc.

Teacher Introduction

Evaluating *Benchmark Assessment* Scores

The goal of each assessment is to evaluate student mastery of previously-taught material and to gauge preparedness for end-of-year testing.

The expectation is for students

- to score 80% or higher on Part 1: Reading (within this score, the expectation is for students to score 80% or higher on the items associated with each Reading Category);
- to score 80% or higher on the multiple-choice portion of Part 2: Writing; and
- to score "3" or higher on their written response to the prompt using the 4-Point Rubric.

For students who do not meet these benchmarks, assign appropriate lessons from the Tier 2 online PDFs. Use student results in particular test categories to guide intervention.

The Answer Keys in *Benchmark Assessment* have been constructed to provide the information needed to aid understanding of student performance.

This column lists the instructional content that is assessed in each item.

Question	Correct Answer	Content Focus	CCSS	Complexity

This column lists the CCSS alignment for each assessment item.

This column lists the Depth of Knowledge associated with each item.

Question	Correct Answer	Content Focus	CCSS	Complexity
43	B	Main Idea and Key Details	RI.5.2	DOK 2
44	I	Context Clues	L.5.4a	DOK 2
45	A	Prefix *re-*	L.5.4b	DOK I

Reporting Category I 2, 3, 19, 21, 22, 38, 43, 44, 51, 54, 55, 57	/12	%
Reporting Category 2 I, 4, 7, 10, 11, 18, 20, 23, 32, 33, 37, 39–41, 47, 52, 53, 56, 58–60	/21	%
Reporting Category 3 5, 6, 8, 9, 13, 14, 16, 24–31, 42, 45, 46, 48–50	/21	%
Reporting Category 4 12, 15, 17, 34–36	/6	%
Total Reading Score	/60	%

Scoring rows identify items by assessment focus and allow for quick record keeping.

Copyright © The McGraw-Hill Companies, Inc.

Part 1: Reading

Read the passage "The Problem of Pickles" before answering Numbers 1 through 11.

The Problem of Pickles

Shakira had always wanted a dog, but her family had never been able to have one. They moved a lot because of Shakira's mother's job. Sometimes they lived in places that didn't allow pets.

Right now the family was living in Iowa; they had a big house with a yard. Shakira thought her dream might finally come true. She saw a listing for puppies in need of homes, and she fell in love with the profile of a cute little mutt named Meadow. But when Shakira shared the description of Meadow with her parents, their faces fell.

"I'm sorry, sweetie," said her mother sadly. "I want a dog, too, but we'll probably only be in this house for a year before my next promotion. By the time you start junior high, we should be in one place for good. Then I promise we'll get a wonderful dog."

The next day, Shakira was sitting in the school cafeteria with Zoe. The two girls were in the same boat. Zoe's mother was in the military, so she had to move a lot, too.

Instead of laughing and talking a mile a minute as usual, both girls sat staring glumly at the mac and cheese on their plates.

"What's wrong?" asked Zoe.

"I have the same old problem," sighed Shakira. "I want a puppy, but my parents say we can't get one until we stop moving. That won't be for a few more years. What about you?"

"Even worse," sighed Zoe. "I *have* the greatest dog in the world, but the military is sending my mom overseas for six months. I have to move in with my grandmother. Grandma lives in a town house that doesn't allow pets. We might have to give Pickles up for adoption—forever!" Zoe cried and dabbed at her tears with a napkin.

Copyright © The McGraw-Hill Companies, Inc.

GO ON →

"That's terrible!" exclaimed Shakira sympathetically. Then a light bulb went off in her head. "But wait, what if my family and I take care of Pickles while your mom is away? We'll be here until at least June, much more than six months. We have a fenced yard, and I would take such good care of her!"

Zoe stopped crying, but her expression was still sad. "Knowing that I wouldn't have to say good-bye to Pickles forever would mean a lot," she said. "But I'll still have to go months and months without seeing her because my grandmother lives really far away. It will be just terrible to miss my mom and my dog at the same time!"

A light shone in Shakira's eyes. "Maybe you can still see Pickles!" she laughed. "We have a camera on our computer that we use when we call my grandparents. I could call every day after school, and you could see Pickles online!"

"Wow!" said Zoe. "That sounds perfect."

That night at dinner, Shakira took a deep breath before presenting her plan. She explained that she wanted to adopt a dog temporarily for a friend whose mother was a soldier. The dog was house-trained and well behaved. It would need a home for just six months.

"That way I get to enjoy a dog while we're here in Iowa. And Zoe doesn't have to lose her best friend in the whole world!"

She held her breath. Her parents looked at each other.

Then her mom smiled. "That is a wonderful plan, Shakira. Your friend's mother is sacrificing a lot for our country, and we would be proud to help her. But are you sure you will be okay giving up this dog when the time comes?"

Shakira nodded. "It may be hard, but I'll be happy knowing that Pickles is back with Zoe. Besides, I can always visit with her online!"

GO ON →

Copyright © The McGraw-Hill Companies, Inc.

Now answer Numbers 1 through 11. Base your answers on "The Problem of Pickles."

1 Read this sentence from the passage.

> She saw a listing for puppies in need of homes, and
> she fell in love with the profile of a cute little mutt
> named Meadow.

Which meaning of the word *profile* is the same as the one used in the sentence above?

Ⓐ an outline drawing

Ⓑ someone's life story

Ⓒ a written description

Ⓓ view of a face from the side

2 Shakira's parents will not let her adopt Meadow because

Ⓕ they will be moving soon.

Ⓖ their next home may not allow a pet.

Ⓗ Shakira is not able to take care of an animal.

Ⓘ Shakira's house in Iowa is too small for a dog.

3 Where are Shakira and Zoe during their conversation?

Ⓐ in Shakira's backyard

Ⓑ in the school cafeteria

Ⓒ at Zoe's grandmother's house

Ⓓ at the library in front of a computer

GO ON →

Copyright © The McGraw-Hill Companies, Inc.

4 Read these sentences from the passage.

> **The two girls were in the same boat. Zoe's mother was in the military, so she had to move a lot, too.**

What do these sentences tell us about the girls?

(F) They are feeling unhappy.

(G) They are lost and confused.

(H) They are in a similar situation.

(I) They are from the same country.

5 Why is Zoe upset?

(A) Her mother has a serious illness.

(B) Her dog may go up for adoption.

(C) Her family has to move overseas.

(D) Her grandmother lives far away.

6 What does Shakira offer to do?

(F) help Zoe hide Pickles

(G) take care of Pickles for a while

(H) find Zoe a dog to replace Pickles

(I) find someone nice to adopt Pickles

Copyright © The McGraw-Hill Companies, Inc.

GO ON →

7 Read this sentence from the passage.

Then a light bulb went off in her head.

What does this sentence tell you about Shakira?

Ⓐ She gets dizzy.

Ⓑ She gets an idea.

Ⓒ She turns on a lamp.

Ⓓ She bumps into something.

8 What does Shakira mean when she tells Zoe, "Maybe you can still see Pickles!"?

Ⓕ Zoe can see Pickles online every day.

Ⓖ Shakira can give Zoe a photo of Pickles.

Ⓗ Zoe can take care of Pickles on weekends.

Ⓘ Shakira can bring Pickles to Zoe's new house.

9 What does Shakira do after she gets home from school?

Ⓐ She writes a description of Pickles.

Ⓑ She tells her parents about her idea.

Ⓒ She gets a camera for her computer.

Ⓓ She calls her grandmother for advice.

Copyright © The McGraw-Hill Companies, Inc.

GO ON →

Name: _____ **Date:** _____

10 What is the theme of this passage?

ⓏF Friends can help each other.

ⓐG Never leave home without saying good-bye.

ⓑH Technology creates as many problems as it solves.

ⓒI A student must work hard at school in order to succeed.

11 Read this sentence from the passage.

"That's terrible!" exclaimed Shakira sympathetically.

The word *sympathetically* has two Greek roots: *sym*, meaning "together or with" and *pathos*, meaning "emotion." What does *sympathetically* mean?

ⒶA in a loud way

ⒷB in a selfish way

ⒸC with shared feelings

ⒹD with help from others

Copyright © The McGraw-Hill Companies, Inc.

Read the article "From City to the Wilderness" before answering Numbers 12 through 21.

From the City to the Wilderness

People are part of the natural world. We depend upon natural resources such as sunlight, water, and food to survive. We share the planet with animals, birds, and insects. We are affected by the weather and by natural disasters such as earthquakes and floods.

Human beings also have an impact on the natural world. We cut down forests, and we change the way that rivers flow. We dig gold and drill oil out of the earth, and throw away mountains of trash. Our actions can help or hurt nature.

Long ago, most people lived close to nature. They hunted and farmed for their food. They knew which plants they could use for medicines when they got sick. When they took long journeys, they used the stars overhead to tell their direction. Ancient people realized that they needed to understand nature and take care of natural resources. Their lives depended on it.

A Faraway Place

Today, many people live in cities. They buy food in shiny supermarkets instead of growing it themselves. Electric lights blot out the stars at night. The temperature inside their homes is always the same, no matter what the weather is like outside.

To a lot of city children, nature seems strange. The wilderness is something that exists in an adventure movie, not in real life. Ordinarily, city children see trees and squirrels in a local park. They might spot a hawk nesting on a tall building or enjoy a few wildflowers blooming in a vacant lot. But many children have no direct experience of the wilderness with its power and beauty.

Copyright © The McGraw-Hill Companies, Inc.

GO ON →

A Program in Minnesota

Across the United States, there are many programs in outdoor education for city children. One such program started in Minnesota in 2010. The program is run by a large local school system along with the National Park Service. The goal is to serve 20,000 city students over three years. Elementary, middle school, and high school students are given the chance to explore the Mississippi River through both day trips and overnight camping experiences. Children learn to canoe and fish. They not only have fun; they begin to see the world through different eyes. They come to understand the environment and why they should help care for it. Then perhaps when they grow up, they will do their part to conserve natural resources.

From Denver to the Mountains

A similar program takes place in the mountains of Colorado. Youths from the city of Denver go to the mountains on wilderness adventures. They start out with short day hikes. If they do well, they can take part in overnight camping and more difficult activities, such as climbing. Some may even take part in trips to out-of-state places, such as Grand Teton National Park.

Many children growing up in a city like Denver have never imagined themselves climbing a mountain. At first, they find the wilderness strange and frightening. They probably also find it boring. Where are the TVs and electronic games?

But these children learn fast. They memorize the names of birds and wildflowers. They begin to appreciate their job in protecting the wilderness. They realize that it is important to carry out everything they bring in, such as food wrappers and water bottles. They also learn wilderness survival skills.

These children from Denver begin to see themselves as part of the natural world. Many of them decide to give back. Some plant trees in areas that no longer have forests. Others build trails for future hikers.

Copyright © The McGraw-Hill Companies, Inc.

GO ON →

Finding Nature in the City

Not all wilderness adventure programs take city children to faraway places. A program called Chicago Adventure Therapy (CAT) helps kids explore the wonderful natural resources inside Chicago!

Andrea Knepper is the founder of CAT. In addition to being a wilderness guide, she is a social worker, or someone who helps people with problems in their daily lives.

Andrea often worked with children in her job as a social worker. Many of these children had trouble following rules. Some of them were scared. Others were angry. Andrea noticed that when these children went outside, they relaxed a little.

Andrea Knepper decided to start a nature program for teens who had seldom had the chance to leave their neighborhoods. She took children on bicycle and climbing trips in the parks and bike trails within the city. She taught some of them to travel on small canoes on Lake Michigan. Taking part in these exciting outdoor activities made a big impression on the youths. They felt physically stronger. They also learned how to solve problems by trusting others, communicating clearly, and working together.

Andrea uses her program to teach city children about nature. But she also uses nature to teach kids about themselves and about life.

Timeline of Chicago Adventure Therapy

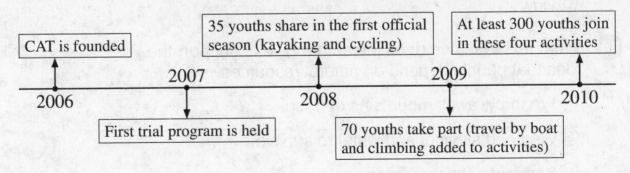

Copyright © The McGraw-Hill Companies, Inc.

Now answer Numbers 12 through 23. Base your answers on "From the City to the Wilderness."

12 What is the main idea of "From the City to the Wilderness"?

Ⓕ Children today have no need to learn about the natural world.

Ⓖ City youths often know more about the wilderness than youths from the country.

Ⓗ Even city youths are affected by natural events such as earthquakes and floods.

Ⓘ Wilderness education programs teach city children about nature and about themselves.

13 Read these sentences from the article.

Human beings also have an impact on the natural world. We cut down forests, and we change the way that rivers flow.

What does the word *impact* mean in the sentence above?

Ⓐ effect

Ⓑ need

Ⓒ opinion

Ⓓ view

14 What text evidence does the author give to support the idea that people depend on natural resources?

Ⓕ We throw away mountains of trash.

Ⓖ We need sunlight and water to survive.

Ⓗ Some see the wilderness as something in an adventure movie.

Ⓘ It is hard to see the stars at night in a city because of electricity.

Copyright © The McGraw-Hill Companies, Inc.

GO ON →

15 Based on text evidence, with which statement would the author most likely agree?

Ⓐ Life today is so much better than long ago.

Ⓑ Cities are the most exciting places in which to live.

Ⓒ People should learn to appreciate and care for the environment.

Ⓓ There is no way to change people and make them act differently.

16 Read this sentence from the article.

Andrea Knepper is the founder of CAT.

Which word has the same Latin root as *founder*?

Ⓕ foul

Ⓖ fondness

Ⓗ foundation

Ⓘ under

17 How is Chicago Adventure Therapy (CAT) different from the other programs that the author describes?

Ⓐ It helps children explore nature inside the city.

Ⓑ It is designed to teach youth about living in the city.

Ⓒ It teaches children about how to care for the environment.

Ⓓ It teaches city children to climb hills and to hike wilderness trails.

Copyright © The McGraw-Hill Companies, Inc.

GO ON →

18 How did Andrea Knepper get the idea for a wilderness program for Chicago youth?

Ⓕ She read about a program for youth in Denver.

Ⓖ She noticed that children were more relaxed outside.

Ⓗ She was tired of being a social worker in city neighborhoods.

Ⓘ She realized that there was no natural beauty inside city limits.

19 How does the author support the point that wilderness programs can help city children begin to care for nature?

Ⓐ Many children in the Denver program go on short hikes.

Ⓑ Some children in the Minnesota program go hunting and fishing.

Ⓒ Most children in the Chicago program learn a lot about themselves.

Ⓓ Some children in the Denver program help plant new trees and build trails.

20 Based on text evidence, the author chose "A Faraway Place" as the subheading because

Ⓕ nature is best seen in a movie.

Ⓖ nature is always a long distance away.

Ⓗ nature seems like an unreal place to city children.

Ⓘ nature is best experienced during a long trip away from the city.

Copyright © The McGraw-Hill Companies, Inc.

GO ON →

21 Why is a timeline included with the passage about Chicago Adventure Therapy (CAT)?

Ⓐ The timeline provides a history of CAT.

Ⓑ An outline of the trial program is given.

Ⓒ The timeline presents the schedule of events held each year.

Ⓓ The timeline shows the increase and decrease of memberships.

22 Based on the timeline, what change has taken place in CAT over the years?

Ⓕ CAT has spread to other cities.

Ⓖ More youths have joined CAT.

Ⓗ CAT has separated into two groups.

Ⓘ CAT has scheduled fewer and fewer activities.

23 Which subheading in the article gives the most information about a program that allows students to explore the Mississippi River?

Ⓐ A Faraway Place

Ⓑ A Program in Minnesota

Ⓒ Finding Nature in the City

Ⓓ From Denver to the Mountains

Copyright © The McGraw-Hill Companies, Inc.

GO ON →

Read the passage "Ant Farm" before answering Numbers 24 through 34.

Ant Farm

Murphy's dad ran an excavating business. Basically, this meant that he dug big holes. When Murphy was really little, watching his dad operate an excavator was his favorite thing in the whole world! He loved the big yellow machines with their sticks and buckets and giant wheels. He admired the smooth way they turned around, and the way his dad could open and close the huge shovel from inside his cab. The best part was when his father used the excavator to pick up a giant rock as easily as if it were a tiny pebble.

When Murphy was three, his dad made him a video of the excavator in action. Murphy used to watch it over and over until everyone in the family begged him to switch to something else!

Now that he was ten, Murphy had added to his list of interests. He liked soccer and math. He had an ant farm, and he was excellent at electronic games. He had lots of friends. But sometimes on summer days, Murphy would accompany his father to a job site and watch a little excavation.

One July morning, Murphy was sitting at the desk in his bedroom. He was slurping down cereal and watching his ants. The farm was actually a big clear plastic box, and through the sides he could observe the insects. They made complicated tunnels and used their antennae to communicate. For the first time, it occurred to him that the ants were excavators, too!

"Murph," his father called from the foot of the stairs, "I'm going on a new assignment today. We're digging foundations for a housing development out in Fitchburg. Want to tag along?"

Murphy jumped up and said, "Bye, ants." As he started to turn away, he could swear that one of the ants waved his feelers at Murphy. Sometimes it really felt as if he and the ants were talking to each other!

Copyright © The McGraw-Hill Companies, Inc.

GO ON →

When they reached the job site, Dad looked around for a spot from which his son could watch the action. He always called this the Observation Deck, even though it wasn't really a deck. This time it was an upward-sloping piece of ground. It was a safe distance away from the area marked out for the foundation. Dad knew that construction could be a dangerous business. Murphy understood that if he ever ran onto the field near the machines, he would never get to come along again.

Murphy watched in anticipation as his father started up the excavator and moved toward a marked-out area. The arm extended, the digger lowered, and Murphy waited for the first big satisfying scoop of dirt.

Instead, there was a loud, clanging noise like a toddler banging on a metal pot with a spoon. Instead of carving deeply into the ground, the excavator bounced along the surface. Dad tried the move again. This time it made a louder clang.

Murphy was on pins and needles trying to figure out what was going on. But he knew better than to leave his post. A tall man in a hard hat walked out to talk to his dad. Murphy could hear a few words of their conversation: "solid bedrock" . . . "find just the right spot" . . . "expensive!"

Something tickled Murphy's right leg. It was an ant. Murphy gently blew it away. But the ant turned back and tickled his leg again with its feelers.

Curiously, Murphy bent over until his eyes were nearly level with the tiny creature. It was waving its feelers frantically as if trying to send the boy a message. Maybe it came from watching his ants at home for so long, but Murphy suddenly felt as if he could understand! The ant was waving its antennae in a certain direction.

Copyright © The McGraw-Hill Companies, Inc.

GO ON →

Murphy stood up and waved his arms in the air to get his father's attention. His father stuck his head out of the cab and yelled, "What is it?"

Murphy cupped his hands together to make his voice carry. "Try backing up a little," he called. "I think you'll find a better spot to dig."

Dad stared for a second, looking baffled. Then he muttered, "Why not?" He backed up the excavator about five feet. The bucket swung through the air, dipped, and cut smoothly into the ground. Murphy watched as Dad wiggled the bucket around. It reminded him of when he was six or seven and trying to extract one of his baby teeth!

Slowly the bucket rose up, carrying the most gigantic rock Murphy had ever seen. Cheers broke out from all of the workers.

Later, Murphy's father asked, "How on Earth did you know I should approach that spot from a few feet back? That was weird!"

Murphy thought hard. Should he open up and tell his father that he could communicate with insects? He decided against it. "I just, er, saw something," he mumbled.

"It's a good thing. You just saved the boss a lot of money and earned me a bonus. I think you should get something out of this, too. Do you have any requests?"

"Ummm," said Murphy, "there's this new kind of ant farm…"

"If you say so, buddy!" laughed his father.

Copyright © The McGraw-Hill Companies, Inc.

GO ON →

Now answer Numbers 24 through 34. Base your answers on "Ant Farm."

24 When Murphy was little, what was his favorite thing to do?

(F) look at ants

(G) wiggle his teeth

(H) play video games

(I) watch his dad dig

25 Read these sentences from the passage.

> **Murphy watched as Dad wiggled the bucket around. It reminded him of when he was six or seven and trying to extract one of his baby teeth!**

What does the word *extract* mean in this sentence?

(A) see

(B) brush

(C) pull out

(D) show off

26 Based on text evidence, which detail best shows that Dad is a careful person?

(F) He made a video for Murphy.

(G) He asks Murphy to come to the new job site.

(H) He tells Murphy to stay on the Observation Deck.

(I) He clangs the excavator on the dirt a second time.

27 Read this sentence about an ant from the passage.

> It was waving its feelers frantically as if trying to send the boy a message.

Why does the author make the ant seem human?

Ⓐ to show that the ant is very small

Ⓑ to show that the boy is very large

Ⓒ to show that the ant is upset by the digging

Ⓓ to show that the boy thinks ants talk to him

28 Read these sentences from the passage.

> Murphy was on pins and needles trying to figure out what was going on. But he knew better than to leave his post.

What mood does the author create in these sentences?

Ⓕ anxious

Ⓖ happy

Ⓗ sad

Ⓘ terrifying

Copyright © The McGraw-Hill Companies, Inc.

29 How does Murphy figure out how to solve his father's problem?

Ⓐ He communicates with an ant.

Ⓑ He talks to the man in the hard hat.

Ⓒ He looks carefully at the excavator.

Ⓓ He remembers something from a video.

30 What happens after Murphy's father moves the excavator back a few feet?

Ⓕ The bucket makes a louder clang.

Ⓖ He can get the bucket under the rock.

Ⓗ The bucket scrapes along the top of the earth.

Ⓘ He cannot lower the bucket all the way down.

31 Read these sentences from the passage.

Should he open up and tell his father that he could communicate with insects? He decided against it.

What does it mean to *open up*?

Ⓐ reveal a secret

Ⓑ act very quickly

Ⓒ proceed very slowly

Ⓓ ask his father's permission

Copyright © The McGraw-Hill Companies, Inc.

GO ON →

32 What is the theme of this passage?

    Ⓕ Follow your feelings.

    Ⓖ Holidays are good for families.

    Ⓗ People should not destroy nature.

    Ⓘ It is important to remember the past.

33 What was Murphy's feeling when visiting his father's workplace?

    Ⓐ The loud noise of the digger frightened Murphy.

    Ⓑ Murphy disliked having to stay on the Observation Deck.

    Ⓒ Murphy enjoyed watching his father operate the digger.

    Ⓓ Excavation work bored Murphy, who would rather watch ants.

34 Which word best describes Dad's feeling at first when Murphy tells him to move the excavator back a few feet?

    Ⓕ angry

    Ⓖ grateful

    Ⓗ puzzled

    Ⓘ sorry

Copyright © The McGraw-Hill Companies, Inc.

GO ON →

Read the article "Animal Tracks and Burrows" before answering Numbers 35 through 43.

Animal Tracks and Burrows

Many wild animals are shy and hard to see. They move quickly and hide in tall grass and leafy trees. They often blend in with their surroundings because of their coloring. However, wildlife biologists have written many books about the signs animals leave. If you learn about these clues, you can become an animal detective. This is a very interesting hobby.

Tracks

The police sometimes look for footprints to help find criminals. Animal detectives look for tracks. Animal tracks show up best in sand, snow, and mud.

Each kind of animal has a different footprint. But some groups of animals make tracks that share certain characteristics. One important feature is the number of toes.

Four Toes in Front, Four in Back

Dogs and their close relatives (coyotes, foxes, and wolves) have four toes on their front paws and four toes on their back paws. So do the wild members of the cat family, such as bobcats and mountain lions. Other animals with two sets of four toes are rabbits.

Four Toes in Front, Five in Back

Rodents have four toes in front and an extra, fifth toe on each rear paw. Rodents include rats, mice, squirrels, and chipmunks.

Copyright © The McGraw-Hill Companies, Inc.

GO ON →

Five and Five

Weasels have five toes in front and in back. So do otters, fishers, and badgers, which are related to weasels. So do raccoons, and so do skunks. (So watch out if you see fresh five-and-five tracks!)

Two Toes

Some animals, including deer, have two "toes." They don't look like other animal toes, though. These animals have hard hooves. Each hoof is split in two parts.

If an animal leaves behind a clear track on a muddy riverbank or in a snowy field, it is easy to count the exact number of toe marks. However, a track is often blurred because the animal was moving quickly or because rain or wind erased some of the details. For this reason, a good animal detective memorizes the general shape of a track. It might be round, oval, or square.

Animal trackers also know how to interpret the pattern of tracks an animal leaves behind as it moves. The way the animal moves is called its "gait." Some animals walk, while others hop. You can tell which is which by looking at their tracks.

Animal Burrows and Holes

A good animal detective looks for more than tracks. For example, he or she learns to identify the holes of animals that burrow, or dig in the ground for shelter. Important things to check for are the size, shape, and location of the hole. These are all clues to the animal that made it.

Eastern mole

This little creature leaves a pile of dirt over the entrance to its burrow, or shelter. The pile is cone-shaped.

Animal Gait Patterns

| Walker | Hopper |

Copyright © The McGraw-Hill Companies, Inc.

Meadow vole

The entry into this animal's burrow is a small hole no more than two inches across. It is found in open, grassy fields.

Eastern chipmunk

The chipmunk's hole is the same size as that of the meadow vole, but there is one big difference. The eastern chipmunk usually digs its burrow near a stone wall.

Woodchucks and badgers

If you see a 12-inch entrance, the burrow could belong to a woodchuck or a badger. If the burrow is in a wooded area, it is likely home to a woodchuck.

Mole

The distinctive sign of a mole is not a visible entrance. Rather, it is the tunnel itself. Moles tunnel close to the surface. They raise the soil above the tunnel in a long mound. If the mole tunnel is in a swampy area, it may belong to a funny-looking creature called a star-nosed mole. If it is in a hilly area, it may belong to an eastern mole.

Track Shapes

Track	Shape	Example	Animals
Cross			rodents (mice, rats, squirrels)
Round			mountain lion, bobcat, lynx
Oval			Dog-like animals, such as fox, coyote
Heart			deer
Box			weasel, mink, wolverine, badger, otter

Copyright © The McGraw-Hill Companies, Inc.

GO ON →

Now answer Numbers 35 through 43. Base your answers on "Animal Tracks and Burrows."

35 What is the main idea of this article?

Ⓐ Wild animals are very shy.

Ⓑ Children need interesting hobbies.

Ⓒ You can identify animals by the signs they leave.

Ⓓ Animals have different numbers of toes on their paws.

36 Read this sentence from the article.

> **However, wildlife biologists have written many books about the signs animals leave.**

What does the root *bio* mean in the word *biologists*?

Ⓕ heat

Ⓖ life

Ⓗ time

Ⓘ water

37 Which is an example of an animal that has four toes in front and five in back?

Ⓐ bobcat

Ⓑ coyote

Ⓒ mouse

Ⓓ weasel

Copyright © The McGraw-Hill Companies, Inc.

GO ON →

38 What text evidence supports the conclusion that animal trackers need to know the general shape of a track?

   Ⓕ Sometimes tracks get blurred.

   Ⓖ Animal tracks are different sizes.

   Ⓗ Tracks show up best in mud and snow.

   Ⓘ Some animals have hooves instead of toes.

39 What text evidence supports the author's point that there is more than one way to track an animal?

   Ⓐ This is a very interesting hobby.

   Ⓑ Animal tracks show up best in sand, snow, and mud.

   Ⓒ But some groups of animals make tracks that share certain characteristics.

   Ⓓ For example, he or she learns to identify the holes of animals that burrow, or dig in the ground for shelter.

40 Which animal makes a raised tunnel just below the surface of the soil?

   Ⓕ badger

   Ⓖ chipmunk

   Ⓗ mole

   Ⓘ vole

Copyright © The McGraw-Hill Companies, Inc.

GO ON →

41 What information can you find using the chart on page 23?

Ⓐ what size a raccoon track is

Ⓑ how many toes a chipmunk has

Ⓒ what animal leaves a round track

Ⓓ what a chipmunk hole looks like

42 What shape track would a rat leave?

Ⓕ oval

Ⓖ round

Ⓗ square

Ⓘ cross-shaped

43 Read these sentences from the article.

> **Important things to check for are the size, shape, and location of the hole. These are all clues to the animal that made it.**

Which meaning of the word *check* is the same as the one used in these sentences?

Ⓐ make a mark next to

Ⓑ examine carefully

Ⓒ stop suddenly

Ⓓ put away

Copyright © The McGraw-Hill Companies, Inc.

GO ON →

Now read the passage "Speaking the Same Language" before answering Numbers 44 through 53.

Speaking the Same Language

On the first day of school, I noticed a new girl sitting in the front row. She was wearing a navy blue skirt and a white button-down shirt. Her hair was in long braids tied with ribbons.

The teacher welcomed everybody. Then she announced, "Class, this is Fiona. She just moved here from England. I am sure you will be especially welcoming and help her with any questions she may have about school."

When the bell rang for lunch, everyone started to rush out the door. The new girl looked a little lost, so I decided to go out on a limb and introduce myself. (Usually I wait for other people to talk to me first.) I said, "Hi, my name is Nina. I love your braids!"

"My what?" asked the girl.

"You know, your *braids*," I repeated. I could feel myself blushing and started to wish I hadn't spoken up.

"Oh," the girl laughed, "my plaits. We call them plaits in England. I'm sorry, I feel as if I speak a completely different language sometimes. May I sit with you in the canteen today?"

Now it was my turn to be completely baffled. I thought a canteen was used for carrying water on a hike. How could you possibly sit in one, and why would you want to?

Copyright © The McGraw-Hill Companies, Inc.

GO ON →

"She means the cafeteria," piped up my bossy friend, Audrey. She joined us as we walked down the crowded hallway. "My mom is from England. We go there every summer to visit my relatives, so I can help translate."

"Brilliant!" exclaimed Fiona.

I have to admit that Audrey was very helpful in the lunch line. First, Fiona asked the server for extra *courgettes*. Audrey quickly said, "She means zucchini." Then Fiona asked if the *biscuits* had any nuts in them. Audrey translated, "Cookies."

"Goodness," sighed Fiona when they sat down with their trays and started eating. "That was exhausting. How am I supposed to remember all of these new words? I'll probably get confused, and then the lunch servers will think I'm completely *daft*!"

"Crazy?" I guessed. Both Fiona and Audrey nodded! I was catching on.

Over lunch, we all got to know each other. I really liked Fiona, but sometimes I felt a little left out. Once she said she forgot to take a *serviette* (a napkin). Then she wished she had some *clingfilm* (plastic wrap) so she could wrap up her second cookie for a snack. Audrey nodded, clearly understanding what these British English terms referred to, but I had no idea!

At the end of the school day, we all rode home on the same bus. Fiona plopped into a seat next to Audrey. I was going to take a seat behind them, but Fiona must have noticed my disappointed expression. She squeezed in to make room for me, too.

Fiona started looking at a flyer about after-school activities. Ms. Lopez had handed them out at the end of the day. After quickly running her finger down the list, Fiona frowned.

"I'm so disappointed that there's no football!"

Copyright © The McGraw-Hill Companies, Inc.

GO ON →

I began to explain that football was more of a high school sport in America. Then Audrey interrupted. "She means soccer, Nina. You mean soccer, Fiona. See, soccer practice starts next week!"

I couldn't take it anymore! I was the one who had walked up to the new girl first to try to make her feel comfortable and welcomed, but Audrey was taking over.

"Stop acting like such a know-it-all, Audrey!" I burst out. "Just because you go to England every summer doesn't mean you know everything about everything!"

Audrey looked shocked. She was quiet for a minute. Then she said, "I'm sorry, I don't mean to act like a know-it-all. Actually, I don't understand a lot of the things Fiona says. Like, what did you mean when you said you like my *trainers*, Fiona?"

Fiona giggled and pointed at Audrey's shoes.

"I have an idea," Fiona said. "The three of us can make an English-American dictionary. It will give translations of all the terms that are different between the two countries. I can use it to learn American English. You two can use it if you want to speak my brand of British English sometimes. Can you both come over to my house this weekend to get started?"

Audrey and I nodded.

"Genius!" said Fiona.

Copyright © The McGraw-Hill Companies, Inc.

GO ON →

Now answer Numbers 44 through 53. Base your answers on the passage "Speaking the Same Language."

44 Which statement by Nina best shows that she is a shy person?

    Ⓕ I noticed a new girl sitting in the front row.

    Ⓖ I have to admit that Audrey was very helpful.

    Ⓗ Now it was my turn to be completely baffled.

    Ⓘ Usually I wait for other people to talk to me first.

45 What is Fiona's main problem?

    Ⓐ She is homesick for her friends in England.

    Ⓑ She will not be able to play sports in America.

    Ⓒ She uses words that many Americans do not understand.

    Ⓓ She is afraid to admit that she is confused by many things.

46 Read this sentence from the passage.

    The new girl looked a little lost, so I decided to go out on a limb and introduce myself.

The phrase "go out on a limb" shows that Nina feels

    Ⓕ happy.   Ⓗ uncomfortable.

    Ⓖ proud.   Ⓘ unlucky.

47 Based on the context, what meaning of *brilliant* is being used in the second paragraph of page 28?

    Ⓐ bright

    Ⓑ great

    Ⓒ smart

    Ⓓ unique

GO ON →

Copyright © The McGraw-Hill Companies, Inc.

48 Audrey helps Fiona in the lunch line by

Ⓕ making sure Fiona gets the food she wants.

Ⓖ helping her find the trays, spoons, knives, and forks.

Ⓗ translating Fiona's words for the lunch servers.

Ⓘ deciding what sandwiches and desserts Fiona should pick.

49 What text evidence best shows that Fiona cares about Nina's feelings?

Ⓐ the way she squeezes over in the seat on the bus

Ⓑ the way she nods when Nina guesses what *daft* means

Ⓒ the way she acts confused when Nina talks about her braids

Ⓓ the way she acts after reading the list of after-school activities

50 Read this sentence from the passage.

Fiona started looking at a flyer about after-school activities.

The Latin root *act* suggests that *activities* are things that people

Ⓕ do.   Ⓗ see.

Ⓖ say.   Ⓘ want.

51 In what way is the setting of this passage most different from Fiona's home in England?

Ⓐ the way girls act

Ⓑ the words people use

Ⓒ the kinds of food available

GO ON →

Copyright © The McGraw-Hill Companies, Inc.

52 Based on Nina's comments, the reader can tell at the end of the story that Audrey will

Ⓕ write the book herself.

Ⓖ stop talking to Nina.

Ⓗ keep interrupting Nina and Fiona.

Ⓘ include everyone in the conversation.

53 What is the main difference between Audrey and Nina?

Ⓐ Audrey likes Fiona more.

Ⓑ Audrey is a better student.

Ⓒ Audrey is more confident.

Ⓓ Audrey likes soccer more.

Copyright © The McGraw-Hill Companies, Inc.

GO ON →

Read the article "The War Against Malaria" before answering Numbers 54 through 60.

The War Against Malaria

Malaria is a disease that is carried by mosquitoes. The symptoms include fever, headache, and chills. If the disease is not treated, it can be deadly, especially in people who are very young or very old.

Where and When Is Malaria Common?

Malaria is common in many parts of Africa. It is also a problem in certain parts of South Asia, the Middle East, and Latin America. In 2010, 225 million cases of this disease were reported around the world. The good news is that, in some countries, malaria has been eliminated. For example, Morocco in northwestern Africa is now free of this disease.

Because malaria is carried by mosquitoes, and because mosquitoes breed in water, malaria is more common during the rainy season. Also, most malaria-carrying mosquitoes bite at night, so that is the time when people need to protect themselves.

How Can Malaria Be Fought?

Malaria can be fought in a number of ways.

Today, there is no workable vaccine, or medicine, against malaria. However, the World Health Organization is currently studying a possible vaccine. Someday soon there may be a safe vaccine to prevent this serious disease.

For those who become ill with malaria, there is treatment. Individuals who show symptoms, or signs, of the disease are first given a test. The test provides results very quickly. If the person actually has malaria, he or she is treated with a group of medicines called ACT.

Copyright © The McGraw-Hill Companies, Inc.

GO ON →

The best way to fight malaria is to keep people from getting sick in the first place. One approach is to spray insect-killing chemicals, or insecticides, in houses. An even better method is sleeping under an insecticide-treated mosquito net, or ITN. A chemical that kills mosquitoes is applied to this kind of tent.

Malaria Fighters

The United Nations has been fighting malaria for years. Today, governments and charities all over the world are distributing ITNs to people in need.

In 2006, a man named Rick Reilly wrote a column in *Sports Illustrated* magazine. He asked readers to donate $10 to buy ITNs for people in Africa. Reilly's article sparked a successful campaign called Nothing But Nets. The National Basketball Association, The Bill and Melinda Gates Foundation, and hundreds of thousands of ordinary people have worked together so far to buy nets and save lives.

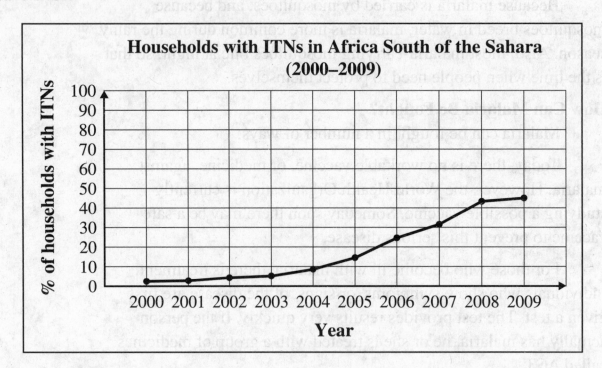

Households with ITNs in Africa South of the Sahara (2000–2009)

Copyright © The McGraw-Hill Companies, Inc.

GO ON →

Now answer Numbers 54 through 60. Base your answers on "The War Against Malaria."

54 Read these sentences from the article.

> **The good news is that, in some countries, malaria has been eliminated. For example, Morocco in northwestern Africa is now free of this disease.**

What is the meaning of *eliminated*?

(F) treated fairly

(G) studied carefully

(H) reduced greatly

(I) destroyed completely

55 What evidence in the text best shows that malaria is a dangerous disease?

(A) Malaria is transmitted by mosquitoes.

(B) If the disease is not treated, it can be deadly.

(C) There is no workable vaccine against malaria.

(D) The United Nations has been fighting malaria for years.

56 Based on text evidence, what is the best way to fight malaria?

(F) with a special spray

(G) with special bed nets

(H) with a test for the disease

(I) with medicines called ACT

Copyright © The McGraw-Hill Companies, Inc.

GO ON →

57 Read this sentence from the article.

> **Today there is no workable vaccine, or medicine, against malaria.**

What does *vaccine* mean in the sentence above?

Ⓐ accident   Ⓒ drug

Ⓑ cure   Ⓓ medal

58 In what kind of weather would someone most need to guard against mosquitoes?

Ⓕ warm and rainy   Ⓗ cold and icy

Ⓖ cool and windy   Ⓘ hot and sunny

59 What text evidence best supports the view that the fight against malaria is succeeding?

Ⓐ Some countries are now free of this disease.

Ⓑ The World Health Organization is studying a possible vaccine.

Ⓒ Scientists now know that malaria is carried by mosquitoes.

Ⓓ The National Basketball Association supports Nothing But Nets.

60 What can you learn from the graph at the end of the article?

Ⓕ Very few households in Africa use ITNs today.

Ⓖ The use of ITNs in Africa has increased every year.

Ⓗ The number of people using ITNs changes very little from year to year.

Ⓘ All of the ITNs that people bought with their $10 are being used in one country.

STOP

Copyright © The McGraw-Hill Companies, Inc.

Part 2: Writing

Philip made a two-column chart to organize his ideas for a paper. Use his plan to answer questions 1–4.

Philip's Writing Plan

Early Settlements in North America	
Settlement	**Who Went There**
Jamestown	English settlers
Plymouth	Puritans and Pilgrims
Pacific Ocean	Vasco Núñez de Balboa
St. Augustine	Spanish explorers

Copyright © The McGraw-Hill Companies, Inc.

GO ON →

1 Which name in this chart is off topic and should be removed from the plan?

Ⓐ Jamestown

Ⓑ Plymouth

Ⓒ Pacific Ocean

Ⓓ St. Augustine

2 Which note below is on topic and should be added to the chart?

Ⓕ John Cabot—explorer for England

Ⓖ Massasoit—Native American leader

Ⓗ Hudson—a river in New York

Ⓘ New Amsterdam—Dutch colonists

3 Which note below is on topic and should be added to the chart?

Ⓐ Quebec, Canada—French fur traders

Ⓑ *Mayflower*—landed at Plymouth

Ⓒ Hernando de Soto—explored Mississippi River

Ⓓ Vikings—explored coast of Canada

4 Based on the information in Philip's Writing Plan, what kind of paper is he planning to write?

Ⓕ a paper that tells an entertaining story about the Pilgrims

Ⓖ a paper that tells about people who started settlements in North America

Ⓗ a paper that explains how to start a settlement in North America

Ⓘ a paper that convinces readers to join a settlement in North America

Copyright © The McGraw-Hill Companies, Inc.

GO ON →

The biography below is a first draft that Evan wrote. It contains mistakes. Read the biography to answer questions 5–11.

(1) Michael Faraday was one of the most famous British scientists who ever lived. (2) Faraday was born outside London in 1791 he was the son of a blacksmith. (3) His family was poor, so he had to leave school at a young age. (4) when Faraday was just 14 years old, he got a job binding books? (5) Young Faraday got a lot out of this job! (6) He read many books about science in his spare time. (7) He even did a few simple experiments.

(8) This determined man found another way to educate himself. (9) He went to public lectures. (10) By a very famous scientist named Sir Humphrey Davy. (11) Faraday took such good notes at Davy's lectures Davy hired him as an assistant. (12) Davy took Faraday along on a tour of Europe. (13) How exciting that trip must have been to a poor young man! (14) He met many other important scientists during the journey.

(15) Working under Davy, Faraday learned a lot about physical science. (16) He made many discoveries about how electricity works he created many new terms that are still used today. (17) Faraday's achievements included creating the first electric motor.

Copyright © The McGraw-Hill Companies, Inc.

GO ON →

5 Which of these is a run-on sentence?

Ⓐ Sentence 2

Ⓑ Sentence 3

Ⓒ Sentence 5

Ⓓ Sentence 7

6 What is the correct way to write sentence 4?

Ⓕ when Faraday was just 14 years old, he got a job binding books.

Ⓖ When Faraday was just 14 years old, he got a job binding books?

Ⓗ When Faraday was just 14 years old, he got a job binding books,

Ⓘ When Faraday was just 14 years old, he got a job binding books.

7 What is the complete predicate in sentence 8?

Ⓐ another way to educate himself

Ⓑ This determined man

Ⓒ found another way to educate himself

Ⓓ found

8 Which of these is a fragment?

Ⓕ Sentence 7

Ⓖ Sentence 8

Ⓗ Sentence 9

Ⓘ Sentence 10

Copyright © The McGraw-Hill Companies, Inc.

GO ON →

9 How could sentence 11 best be written?

Ⓐ Faraday took such good notes at Davy's lectures, Davy hired him as an assistant.

Ⓑ Because Faraday took such good notes at Davy's lectures, Davy hired him as an assistant.

Ⓒ Faraday took such good notes at Davy's lectures since Davy hired him as an assistant.

Ⓓ Faraday took such good notes at Davy's lectures, but Davy hired him as an assistant.

10 Which is the correct way to write sentence 16?

Ⓕ He made many discoveries about how electricity works, and he created many new terms that are still used today.

Ⓖ He made many discoveries about how electricity works or he created many new terms that are still used today.

Ⓗ He made many discoveries about how electricity works, but he created many new terms that are still used today.

Ⓘ He made many discoveries about how electricity works, he created many new terms that are still used today.

11 What is the complete subject of sentence 17?

Ⓐ Faraday

Ⓑ Faraday's achievements

Ⓒ included

Ⓓ the first electric motor

Copyright © The McGraw-Hill Companies, Inc.

GO ON →

Read this passage about a new invention. Choose the word or words that correctly complete questions 12–18.

Remote-Control Insects

Scientists are figuring out how to attach tiny ____(12)____ to insects. By doing so, they will turn the bugs into little ____(13)____. These remote-control "spybugs" can be used to spy on people, and they can be used to find lost pets and children.

But how would you like to find out that a butterfly on your windowsill ____(14)____ you! Some of these ____(15)____ ideas sound interesting, but they should not be used in real life.

Recently, I ____(16)____ to the government about this issue. I ____(17)____ hard about the problem. Then I stated my main concern. The government should not be able to enter a ____(18)____ home without good reason. That goes for spybugs, too!

Copyright © The McGraw-Hill Companies, Inc.

GO ON →

12 Which answer should go in blank (12)?

(F) camera

(G) cameras

(H) camera's

13 Which answer should go in blank (13)?

(A) spies

(B) spys

(C) spies'

14 Which answer should go in blank (14)?

(F) watching

(G) has watch

(H) is watching

15 Which answer should go in blank (15)?

(A) scientist's

(B) scientists'

(C) scientists

Copyright © The McGraw-Hill Companies, Inc.

16 Which answer should go in blank (16)?

Ⓕ wrote

Ⓖ write

Ⓗ will write

17 Which answer should go in blank (17)?

Ⓐ thinked

Ⓑ thinking

Ⓒ thought

18 Which answer should go in blank (18)?

Ⓕ persons

Ⓖ persons'

Ⓗ person's

Copyright © The McGraw-Hill Companies, Inc.

GO ON →

The passage below is a journal entry that Katelynn wrote. It contains mistakes. Read the journal entry to answer questions 19–26.

(1) How tired I am of sharing a room! (2) My little sister Rebekah is very nosy. (3) She wants to know everything I am doing she never stops asking questions. (4) She even tries helping with my homework. (5) This is ridiculous since she can't even read yet.

(6) I don't want to be mean. (7) I want some privacy. (8) I've got a great idea. (9) You know that so-called "home office" on the third floor? (10) Ever since Mom got a job selling real estate, she has stopped using it. (11) We could turn it into another bedroom! (12) Dad and I could clear out all of the old junk. (13) Dad and I could paint it.

(14) I will have to present my proposal to Mom and Dad in just the right way. (15) Should I tell them about it tonight after dinner

Copyright © The McGraw-Hill Companies, Inc.

GO ON →

19 Which sentence contains a prepositional phrase that serves as an adverb?

Ⓐ Sentence 2

Ⓑ Sentence 3

Ⓒ Sentence 4

Ⓓ Sentence 5

20 What is the simple subject of sentence 1?

Ⓕ How tired

Ⓖ I

Ⓗ am

Ⓘ sharing a room

21 How could sentence 3 best be written?

Ⓐ She wants to know everything I am doing, or she never stops asking questions.

Ⓑ She wants to know everything I am doing, she never stops asking questions.

Ⓒ She wants to know everything I am doing, but she never stops asking questions.

Ⓓ She wants to know everything I am doing, and she never stops asking questions.

22 How can sentences 6 and 7 best be combined?

Ⓕ I don't want to be mean, I want some privacy.

Ⓖ I don't want to be mean so I want some privacy.

Ⓗ I don't want to be mean, but I want some privacy.

Ⓘ I don't want to be mean, or I want some privacy.

Copyright © The McGraw-Hill Companies, Inc.

GO ON →

23 Which sentence contains a dependent clause?

Ⓐ Sentence 4

Ⓑ Sentence 5

Ⓒ Sentence 8

Ⓓ Sentence 9

24 Which of these is a complex sentence?

Ⓝ Sentence 10

Ⓞ Sentence 11

Ⓟ Sentence 12

Ⓠ Sentence 13

25 Which is the best way to combine sentences 12 and 13?

Ⓐ Dad and I could clear out all of the old junk, Dad and I could paint it.

Ⓑ Dad and I could clear out all of the old junk so Dad and I could paint it.

Ⓒ Dad and I could clear out and paint it, all of the old junk.

Ⓓ Dad and I could clear out all of the old junk and paint it.

26 Which is the best way to write sentence 15?

Ⓝ Should I tell them about it tonight after dinner.

Ⓞ Should I tell them about it tonight after dinner!

Ⓟ Tonight after dinner should I tell them about it!

Ⓠ Should I tell them about it tonight after dinner?

Copyright © The McGraw-Hill Companies, Inc.

Read the passage below. Choose the word or words that correctly complete questions 27–34.

People can use the Internet to answer all kinds of questions. A concerned relative might use it to find out how much damage occurred in an area where several ____(27)____ had just struck. A cook might look up the best way of freezing some leftover ____(28)____ of French bread. A fan might check a sports website to determine who ____(29)____ the winning pitch in a World Series game. Students ____(30)____ it to research anything from how many ____(31)____ are usually born in a litter to what happened during the campaign to allow ____(32)____ to vote.

It is important to realize that not all online information is accurate. If you follow a recipe that contains errors, your Thanksgiving turkey ____(33)____ funny. Always remember to check the source. The homepage of a website will often indicate who ____(34)____ the site together. Sources that end in .gov or .edu are often reliable because they contain information from government experts or teachers.

Copyright © The McGraw-Hill Companies, Inc.

GO ON →

27 Which answer should go in blank (27)?

Ⓐ tornadoes

Ⓑ tornadoies

Ⓒ tornadoses

28 Which answer should go in blank (28)?

Ⓕ loafs

Ⓖ loafies

Ⓗ loaves

29 Which answer should go in blank (29)?

Ⓐ throwed

Ⓑ threw

Ⓒ thrown

30 Which answer should go in blank (30)?

Ⓕ using

Ⓖ can use

Ⓗ has used

Copyright © The McGraw-Hill Companies, Inc.

GO ON →

31 Which answer should go in blank (31)?

Ⓐ foxes

Ⓑ foxs

Ⓒ foxies

32 Which answer should go in blank (32)?

Ⓕ woman

Ⓖ womans

Ⓗ women

33 Which answer should go in blank (33)?

Ⓐ taste

Ⓑ did taste

Ⓒ will taste

34 Which answer should go in blank (34)?

Ⓕ put

Ⓖ putted

Ⓗ putting

Copyright © The McGraw-Hill Companies, Inc.

GO ON →

The set of instructions below is a first draft that Grace wrote. It contains mistakes. Use the instructions to answer questions 35–42.

Making Paper Snowflakes

(1) You should start with a piece of stiff, white paper.

(2) Is it a rectangle or a square

(3) If it is a rectangle, measure the length of the short side.

(4) Then cut the long side it should be the same length.

(5) Now you will have a square piece of paper.

(6) Fold the square in half diagonally it will become a triangle.

(7) The next step is to fold the triangle in half two times.

(8) Cut some little holes in the folded triangle.

(9) The cuts should not go through the unopened side.

(10) When the triangle is opened.

(11) It will turn into a beautiful snowflake

(12) You can tape your paper snowflakes to windows.

Copyright © The McGraw-Hill Companies, Inc.

GO ON →

35 What is the simple predicate of sentence 1?

Ⓐ You

Ⓑ should

Ⓒ start

Ⓓ piece

36 How can sentence 2 best be written?

Ⓕ Is it a rectangle or a square.

Ⓖ Is it a rectangle or a square?

Ⓗ Is it a rectangle or a square!

Ⓘ Is it a rectangle or a square,

37 Which of these is a run-on sentence?

Ⓐ Sentence 4

Ⓑ Sentence 7

Ⓒ Sentence 8

Ⓓ Sentence 10

38 Which word in sentence 3 is a subordinating conjunction?

Ⓕ If

Ⓖ is

Ⓗ measure

Ⓘ of

Copyright © The McGraw-Hill Companies, Inc.

GO ON →

39 How can sentence 6 best be written?

Ⓐ Fold the square in half diagonally, it will become a triangle.

Ⓑ Fold the square in half diagonally, but it will become a triangle.

Ⓒ Fold the square in half diagonally; it will become a triangle.

Ⓓ Fold the square in half diagonally, or it will become a triangle.

40 Which of these is a sentence fragment?

Ⓕ Sentence 3

Ⓖ Sentence 7

Ⓗ Sentence 9

Ⓘ Sentence 10

41 What is the complete subject of sentence 7?

Ⓐ The next

Ⓑ The next step

Ⓒ is to fold

Ⓓ is to fold the triangle in half two times

42 Which word from sentence 9 is a noun in a prepositional phrase?

Ⓕ through

Ⓖ the

Ⓗ unopened

Ⓘ side

Copyright © The McGraw-Hill Companies, Inc.

GO ON →

Read the story below. Choose the word that correctly completes questions 43–50.

One night, Marta was _____(43)_____ in bed reading a book. Suddenly, she heard strange noises right behind her head! Alarmed, she jumped out of bed and called her mother. Her mom heard the alarm in her _____(44)_____ voice and dashed down the hallway.

Marta's mom and Marta listened to the strange skittering, scrambling noises that came from inside the wall.

"It sounds like _____(45)_____ ticking in there," exclaimed Marta, "or maybe _____(46)_____ being torn up."

"My guess is a bunch of squirrels or _____(47)_____," said her mother, frowning.

After school the next day, Marta held the ladder for her mother.

"We have to find out where those animals _____(48)_____ in so we can block the hole," said Marta's mom.

A second later she said, "I _____(49)_____ it! The _____(50)_____ entrance is right here!"

That night, Marta's dad lured the animals out with food and repaired the hole.

Copyright © The McGraw-Hill Companies, Inc.

GO ON →

43 Which answer should go in blank (43)?

  Ⓐ lie

  Ⓑ lieing

  Ⓒ lying

44 Which answer should go in blank (44)?

  Ⓕ daughter's

  Ⓖ daughters

  Ⓗ daughters'

45 Which answer should go in blank (45)?

  Ⓐ watch's

  Ⓑ watches

  Ⓒ watchs

46 Which answer should go in blank (46)?

  Ⓕ leafs

  Ⓖ leafes

  Ⓗ leaves

Copyright © The McGraw-Hill Companies, Inc.

GO ON →

47 Which answer should go in blank (47)?

Ⓐ mouses

Ⓑ mousies

Ⓒ mice

48 Which answer should go in blank (48)?

Ⓕ got

Ⓖ get

Ⓗ getted

49 Which answer should go in blank (49)?

Ⓐ find

Ⓑ finded

Ⓒ found

50 Which answer should go in blank (50)?

Ⓕ squirrels'

Ⓖ squirrel's

Ⓗ squirrels

STOP

Copyright © The McGraw-Hill Companies, Inc.

Benchmark Assessment • Benchmark 1

Writing Prompt – Informative

Whether they live in rural areas, small towns, sprawling suburbs, or big cities, people work together in groups to get things done. Think about an example of people cooperating on a task. The group could be formal (such as government workers) or informal (such as a bunch of neighbors). The task may be something you have experienced yourself or something you have read or heard about.

Write an informative article telling about the people involved in the task or project and what they did. Explain how a single person could not have done this job alone.

Use the space below to plan your writing. Write your final copy on a clean sheet of paper.

_____

_____

_____

_____

_____

_____

_____

_____

_____

_____

_____

Copyright © The McGraw-Hill Companies, Inc.

Name: _____

Question	Correct Answer	Content Focus	CCSS	Complexity
1	C	Context Clues: Multiple-Meaning Words	L.5.4a	DOK 2
2	G	Character, Setting, Plot: Problem and Solution	RL.4.3	DOK 2
3	B	Character, Setting, Plot: Problem and Solution	RL.4.3	DOK 1
4	H	Idioms	L.5.5b	DOK 2
5	B	Character, Setting, Plot: Problem and Solution	RL.4.3	DOK 2
6	G	Character, Setting, Plot: Problem and Solution	RL.4.3	DOK 2
7	B	Idioms	L.5.5b	DOK 2
8	F	Character, Setting, Plot: Problem and Solution	RL.4.3	DOK 2
9	B	Character, Setting, Plot: Sequence	RL.3.3	DOK 2
10	F	Theme	RL.5.2	DOK 3
11	C	Greek and Latin Roots	L.5.4b	DOK 1
12	I	Main Idea and Key Details	RI.5.2	DOK 2
13	A	Context Clues: Sentence Clues	L.5.4a	DOK 2
14	G	Main Idea and Key Details	RI.5.2	DOK 3
15	C	Author's Point of View	RI.5.8	DOK 3
16	H	Latin Roots	L.5.4b	DOK 1
17	A	Main Idea and Key Details	RI.5.2	DOK2
18	G	Main Idea and Key Details	RI.5.2	DOK 2
19	D	Author's Point of View	RI.5.8	DOK 3
20	H	Main Idea and Key Details	RI.5.2	DOK 3
21	A	Text Features: Timelines	RI.4.7	DOK 2
22	G	Text Features: Timelines	RI.4.7	DOK 1
23	B	Text Features: Headings	RI.4.7	DOK 2
24	I	Character, Setting, Plot: Sequence	RL.3.3	DOK 2
25	C	Context Clues: Sentence Clues	L.5.4a	DOK 2

Copyright © The McGraw-Hill Companies, Inc.

Question	Correct Answer	Content Focus	CCSS	Complexity
26	H	Character, Setting, Plot: Character	RL.5.3	DOK 2
27	D	Personification	L.5.5a	DOK 2
28	F	Idioms	L.5.5b	DOK 2
29	A	Character, Setting, Plot: Problem and Solution	RL.4.3	DOK 2
30	G	Character, Setting, Plot: Sequence	RL.3.3	DOK 2
31	A	Idioms	L.5.5b	DOK 2
32	F	Theme	RL.5.2	DOK 3
33	C	Character, Setting, Plot: Problem and Solution	RL.4.3	DOK 2
34	H	Character, Setting, Plot: Character	RL.4.3	DOK 2
35	C	Main Idea and Key Details	RI.5.2	DOK 2
36	G	Greek Roots	L.5.4b	DOK 1
37	C	Main Idea and Key Details	RI.5.2	DOK 2
38	F	Main Idea and Key Details	RI.5.2	DOK 3
39	D	Author's Point of View	RI.5.8	DOK 3
40	H	Main Idea and Key Details	RI.5.2	DOK 2
41	C	Text Features: Charts	RI.4.7	DOK 2
42	I	Text Features: Charts	RI.4.7	DOK 2
43	B	Context Clues: Multiple-Meaning Words	L.5.4a	DOK 2
44	I	Character, Setting, Plot: Character	RL.5.3	DOK 3
45	C	Character, Setting, Plot: Problem and Solution	RL.4.3	DOK 2
46	H	Idioms	L.5.5b	DOK 2
47	B	Context Clues: Multiple-Meaning Words	L.5.4a	DOK 1
48	H	Character, Setting, Plot: Problem and Solution	RL.4.3	DOK 2
49	A	Character, Setting, Plot: Character	RL.5.3	DOK 3
50	F	Latin Roots	L.5.4b	DOK 1

Copyright © The McGraw-Hill Companies, Inc.

Part I: Reading Answer Key

Name: _____

Question	Correct Answer	Content Focus	CCSS	Complexity
51	B	Character, Setting, Plot: Compare and Contrast	RL.5.3	DOK 2
52	I	Character, Setting, Plot: Compare and Contrast	RL.5.3	DOK 2
53	C	Character, Setting, Plot: Compare and Contrast	RL.5.3	DOK 2
54	I	Context Clues: Sentence Clues	L.5.4a	DOK 2
55	B	Main Idea and Key Details	RI.5.2	DOK 3
56	G	Main Idea and Key Details	RI.5.2	DOK 3
57	C	Context Clues: Sentence Clues	L.5.4a	DOK 2
58	F	Main Idea and Key Details	RI.5.2	DOK 2
59	A	Main Idea and Key Details	RI.5.2	DOK 3
60	G	Text Features: Graphs	RI.4.7	DOK 2

Reporting Category 1 1, 11, 13, 16, 25, 36, 43, 47, 50, 54, 57		/11	%
Reporting Category 2 10, 12, 14, 15, 17–20, 32, 35, 37–40, 55, 56, 58, 59		/18	%
Reporting Category 3 2–9, 24, 26–31, 33, 34, 44, 45, 46, 48, 49, 51–53		/25	%
Reporting Category 4 21–23, 41, 42, 60		/6	%
Total Reading Score		/60	%

Copyright © The McGraw-Hill Companies, Inc.

Part 2: Writing Answer Key   Name: _____

Question	Correct Answer	Content Focus	CCSS	Complexity
1	C	Prewriting: Organizing	W.5.2b	DOK 2
2	I	Prewriting: Organizing	W.5.2b	DOK 2
3	A	Prewriting: Organizing	W.5.2b	DOK 2
4	G	Prewriting: Organizing	W.5.2a	DOK 1
5	A	Run-on Sentences and Fragments	L.4.1f	DOK 1
6	I	Sentences	L.4.1f	DOK 1
7	C	Subjects and Predicates	L.4.1f	DOK 1
8	I	Run-on Sentences and Fragments	L.4.1f	DOK 1
9	B	Complex Sentences	L.5.3a	DOK 2
10	F	Compound Sentences and Conjunctions	L.5.1a	DOK 1
11	B	Subjects and Predicates	L.4.1F	DOK 1
12	G	Singular and Plural Nouns	L.5.2	DOK 1
13	A	Singular and Plural Nouns	L.5.2	DOK 1
14	H	Main Verbs and Helping Verbs	L.5.1c	DOK 1
15	B	Possessive Nouns	L.5.2	DOK 1
16	F	Verb Tenses	L.5.1d	DOK 1
17	C	Irregular Verbs	L.5.1c	DOK 1
18	H	Possessive Nouns	L.5.2	DOK 1
19	C	Nouns in Prepositional Phrases	L.5.1a	DOK 1
20	G	Subjects and Predicates	L.4.1f	DOK 1
21	D	Compound Sentences and Conjunctions	L.5.1a	DOK 1
22	H	Compound Sentences and Conjunctions	L.5.3a	DOK 1
23	B	Independent and Dependent Clauses	L.5.2	DOK 1
24	F	Complex Sentences	L.5.2	DOK 1
25	D	Sentence Combining	L.5.3a	DOK 2
26	I	Sentences	L.4.1f	DOK 1
27	A	Plural Nouns	L.5.2	DOK 1
28	H	Plural Nouns	L.5.2	DOK 1

Copyright © The McGraw-Hill Companies, Inc.

Question	Correct Answer	Content Focus	CCSS	Complexity
29	B	Irregular Verbs	L.5.1c	DOK 1
30	G	Main Verbs and Helping Verbs	L.5.1c	DOK 1
31	A	Plural Nouns	L.5.2	DOK 1
32	H	Plural Nouns	L.5.2	DOK 1
33	C	Verb Tenses	L.5.1d	DOK 1
34	F	Irregular Verbs	L.5.1c	DOK 1
35	C	Subjects and Predicates	L.4.1f	DOK 1
36	G	Sentences	L.4.1f	DOK 1
37	A	Run-on Sentences and Fragments	L.4.1f	DOK 1
38	F	Complex Sentences	L.5.2	DOK 1
39	C	Compound Sentences and Conjunctions	L.5.1a	DOK 1
40	I	Run-on Sentences and Fragments	L.4.1f	DOK 1
41	B	Subjects and Predicates	L.4.1f	DOK 1
42	I	Nouns in Prepositional Phrases	L.5.1a	DOK 1
43	C	Main Verbs and Helping Verbs	L.5.1c	DOK 1
44	F	Possessive Nouns	L.5.2	DOK 1
45	B	Singular and Plural Nouns	L.5.2	DOK 1
46	H	Plural Nouns	L.5.2	DOK 1
47	C	Plural Nouns	L.5.2	DOK 1
48	F	Verb Tenses	L.5.1d	DOK 1
49	C	Irregular Verbs	L.5.1c	DOK 1
50	F	Possessive Nouns	L.5.2	DOK 1
Prompt	see below	Informative Writing	W.5.2a–e	DOK 3

Prewriting/Organization 1–4	/4	%
English Language Conventions 5–50	/46	%
Total Writing Score	/50	%

Copyright © The McGraw-Hill Companies, Inc.

Writing Prompt

Refer to scoring criteria in the Teacher Introduction.

Part 1: Reading

Read the article "The Dust Bowl" before answering Numbers 1 through 12.

The Dust Bowl

On April 14, 1935, many people in the Southern Plains of the United States feared the world was coming to an end. A dense black cloud sped toward them like a giant locomotive. It reached from the ground more than 100 feet into the sky. But it was not a rain cloud. It was made up of millions of particles of fine dust, a thick blanket that blocked out the sun.

Everyone rushed to get inside so they would not choke on the dirt. Winds of more than 60 miles an hour drove the dust against cars and buildings. It came into houses through the tiniest cracks, even when the doors and windows were closed and locked.

That day was called "Black Sunday." It brought the worst of the storms in the area called the Dust Bowl.

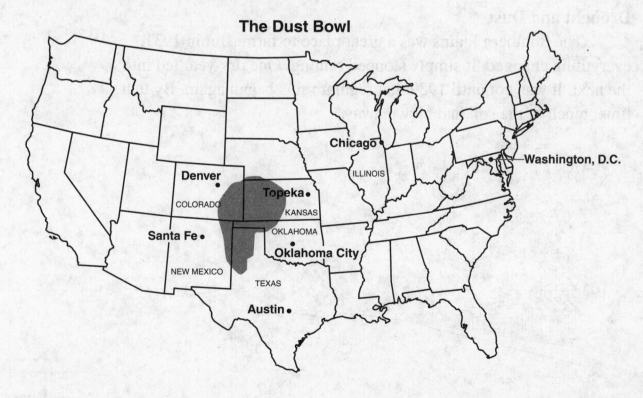

The Dust Bowl

Copyright © The McGraw-Hill Companies, Inc.

GO ON →

Wheat Will Win the War!

During and after World War I, from about 1917–1930, there was a great demand for wheat. Wheat is used to make flour for bread and other products. Huge areas of farmland in Europe were destroyed by the fighting there. People around the world needed wheat from the United States.

The United States government announced that "Wheat Will Win the War!" Americans and their allies would be well fed while their opponents did not have enough food. Farmers knew they could sell all the wheat they raised at good prices.

The Southern Plains offered a perfect spot for wheat farms. The land was flat and covered with low grass and shrubs. With new, powerful tractors, farmers could plow under the grass, leaving the soil ready for planting long, straight rows of wheat. So many people began to grow wheat that some called the period The Great Plow-Under.

There was a great demand for American beef, too. Cattle ranchers increased the size of their herds. The cattle ate so much of the grass that the land was almost as bare as the land for planting wheat.

Drought and Dust

The Southern Plains was a great place to farm. But in 1931, everything changed. It simply stopped raining. One dry year led into the next. It was not until 1939 that regular rains began again. By that time, much of the soil had blown away.

Copyright © The McGraw-Hill Companies, Inc.

GO ON →

Without rain to grow wheat and grass, the upper layer of soil became dry and dusty. There were few trees and plants to hold down this layer. So when the wind raced across the flat fields, the soil was easily blown away. Dust storms became common during the 1930s.

During this period, adults and children wore face masks outside to keep the dust out of their mouths and lungs. Many people became sick and some died from "dust pneumonia" when they breathed in too much dust. Animals in fields died when their stomachs filled with dust.

After years of dust storms, with no crops or income, many people abandoned their land and moved west. They had little money and few household possessions. By the end of the period, one-fourth of all the people had left the area. So many people went to California that guards were sent to the state's borders to try to keep them out.

Government Action

Hugh Bennett was the head of the United States government agency that tried to protect farmland. He had struck out in his earlier attempts to get the government to take action. However, the "Black Sunday" storm reached into the Midwest and East. When it hid the sun in Washington, D.C., Bennett announced to Congress, "This, gentlemen, is what I have been talking about."

Congress passed the Soil Conservation Act soon afterward. The government paid farmers to change their methods of farming so that the topsoil could not be so easily blown away. Farmers rotated their crops and plowed the land in curves instead of straight lines. They also planted trees to slow down the wind. These and other methods reduced by 65% the amount of soil blown away.

The Future

Once the rains returned in 1939, much of the Southern Plains gradually returned to valuable farmland. Some is still barren and dusty. There is currently no way to prevent a drought. Modern farming techniques, however, are able to prevent the return of the Black Blizzards of the 1930s.

Copyright © The McGraw-Hill Companies, Inc.

GO ON →

Now answer Numbers 1 through 12. Base your answers on "The Dust Bowl."

1 Read this sentence from the article.

> **Congress passed the Soil Conservation Act soon afterward.**

Which meaning of the word *passed* is the same as the one used in the sentence above?

Ⓐ went by

Ⓑ voted for

Ⓒ handed to

Ⓓ got a good grade

2 Read this sentence from the article.

> **Americans and their allies would be well fed while their opponents did not have enough food.**

The origin of *opponent* is a Latin word that means "against a place." Which of the following words is most likely to come from that Latin word?

Ⓕ operate

Ⓖ opposite

Ⓗ possess

Ⓘ stopped

3 Why was there a worldwide demand for American wheat and beef during World War I?

Ⓐ The U.S. government said "Wheat Will Win the War."

Ⓑ The Southern Plains was a perfect spot for farming and herding.

Ⓒ Wartime fighting had destroyed huge areas of farmland in Europe.

Ⓓ American farmers had increased their fields and herds.

Copyright © The McGraw-Hill Companies, Inc.

GO ON →

Copyright © The McGraw-Hill Companies, Inc.

4 Which sentence below gives the reader reason to believe that the Southern Plains was a great place to farm before 1931?

F Farmers know they could sell all their wheat at good prices.

G People around the world needed wheat from the United States.

H Huge areas of Europe were destroyed by the fighting there.

I With powerful tractors, farmers could plow under grass and leave the soil ready for planting.

5 The author organized the section "Drought and Dust" by

A stating the pros and cons of raising wheat.

B tracing the causes and effects of dust storms.

C comparing and contrasting life before and after World War I.

D listing in importance the characteristics of an effective leader.

6 Which sentence from the passage supports the author's view that farming has improved through the years?

F On April 14, 1935, many people in the Southern Plains of the United States feared the world was coming to an end.

G So many people began to grow wheat that some called the period The Great Plow-Under.

H Hugh Bennett was the head of the United States government agency that tried to protect farmland.

I Modern farming techniques, however, are able to prevent the return of the Black Blizzards of the 1930s.

GO ON →

7 Read this sentence from the article.

> **There were few trees and plants to hold down this layer. So when the wind raced across the flat fields, the soil was easily blown away.**

What does the expression "the wind raced across the flat fields" mean?

Ⓐ The wind became weaker.

Ⓑ The fields blocked the wind.

Ⓒ The fields seemed friendly.

Ⓓ The wind was very strong.

8 Read this sentence from the article.

> **A dense black cloud sped toward them like a giant locomotive.**

What mood does the author create by using this simile?

Ⓕ brisk   Ⓗ fearful

Ⓖ curious   Ⓘ humorous

9 Read this sentence from the article.

> **He had struck out in his earlier attempts to get the government to take action.**

This sentence shows that Bennett had

Ⓐ made a mistake.

Ⓑ worked very hard.

Ⓒ stopped trying.

Ⓓ failed to get a result.

Copyright © The McGraw-Hill Companies, Inc.

GO ON →

10 The author includes the map in this article in order to show

    Ⓕ major cities in the Dust Bowl.

    Ⓖ areas affected by dust storms.

    Ⓗ farmlands that produced wheat.

    Ⓘ patches of rural land affected by flooding.

11 Read this sentence from the article.

> **After years of dust storms, with no crops or income, many people abandoned their land and moved west.**

Which word has the OPPOSITE meaning of *abandoned* as used in the sentence above?

    Ⓐ fenced

    Ⓑ kept

    Ⓒ farmed

    Ⓓ sold

12 Read this sentence about the dust cloud on "Black Sunday."

> **It was made up of millions of particles of fine dust, a thick blanket that blocked out the sun.**

The author's use of the phrase "a thick blanket" helps the reader understand that the cloud

    Ⓕ was solid and heavy.

    Ⓖ will pass very quickly.

    Ⓗ created hot temperatures.

    Ⓘ seems comforting and peaceful.

Copyright © The McGraw-Hill Companies, Inc.

GO ON →

Read the article "Fighting the War at Home" before answering Numbers 13 through 22.

Fighting the War at Home

World War II affected the lives of nearly all Americans. About one of every eight people served in the military, a total of more than 16 million men and women. More than a million were killed or wounded.

However, not everyone could join the army or navy. Many people could not serve because they were too old or too young. Some had physical problems. Women and African Americans faced other obstacles, such as unfair treatment, that prevented them from joining. Perhaps most important, American workers were needed at home. They had to produce the guns, ammunition, clothing, food, and other supplies to fight the war.

Life was very hard for most of the soldiers. But life at home was a challenge, too. All Americans were asked to make sacrifices so the troops could have what they needed to win the war.

Rationing

When World War II began, the United States was just beginning to recover from the Great Depression. Its farms and factories were not producing at the highest levels. Production had to increase rapidly to equip and feed a large military force stationed overseas. Until production increased, the American people had to use less of many products so more could go to the military.

The federal government met this problem by beginning a rationing program. Rationing means allowing each person to buy or use only a certain amount of something. When there was a shortage of a certain product, the government temporarily controlled how much each person could buy. At different times, rubber tires, gasoline, heating oil, shoes, and many types of foods were rationed.

Copyright © The McGraw-Hill Companies, Inc.

GO ON →

One of the first things rationed was rubber. The Japanese had taken over many rubber plantations in Asia. The United States did not have a supply of raw materials to make rubber. The government asked people to turn in all old automobile and bicycle tires. They couldn't buy more unless they could show a very important need.

For most of the war, people had to use one of the 8,000 ration boards, or offices, that sprouted up around the country. Before they could buy rationed goods, each household had to get a book or coupons or tokens for them. Then they used their ration books to buy the amount the government decided was reasonable for a certain period of time. Even if a family had plenty of money, they could not buy an extra pound of cheese every month. Wealthy families could not buy more shoes than other families.

Most families had to plan their meals carefully to use only the amount that was allowed. At the time, women did most of the shopping, and they studied their ration books carefully before they went to the store. Men tended to do most of the driving and had to carry their gasoline rations with them each time they needed to fill up. Many people treated their ration books like gold.

The government even controlled women's clothing to force conservation of products needed by the military. For example, skirts were made with hems that were turned under at the bottom. It was a part of the skirt that was not seen. The government reduced wasted cloth by stating that the hems could not be more than two inches wide. They limited the width of women's leather belts to two inches as well.

Victory Gardens

American farmers could not supply enough food at the beginning of the war. They needed to feed people at home as well as the military and America's allies. The U.S. government encouraged people to plant small vegetable gardens wherever there were good spots. Many people turned their lawns into gardens. In this way, they were able to eat fresh vegetables that were not available at the stores. Many cities and towns let people plant gardens in park areas.

Copyright © The McGraw-Hill Companies, Inc.

GO ON →

The U.S. government established the Office of War Information to support rationing, small gardens, and other programs. This office published news articles, posters, and short movies to show how important it was for people at home to support the war. To feel good about gardening, people named the small gardens "Victory Gardens." By planting gardens, Americans were helping their troops achieve victory.

Shared Sacrifice

When the war was over, Americans were happy to return to a life without rationing, Victory Gardens, or any of the other sacrifices they had to make. On the other hand, many people had some fond memories of the sacrifices they made during the war. It felt good for everyone to work together. People were not always as comfortable as they would have liked. However, they at home were helping to fight the war, and they felt a part of the victory in the end.

Wartime Rationing (1942–1945)

Rationed Items	Rationing Period
Tires	January 1942–December 1945
Gasoline	May 1942–August 1945
Shoes	February 1943–October 1945
Sugar	May 1942–December 1947
Coffee	November 1942–July 1943
Cheese	March 1943–November 1945
Meat	March 1943–November 1945

Copyright © The McGraw-Hill Companies, Inc.

GO ON →

Now answer Numbers 13 through 22. Base your answers on "Fighting the War at Home."

13 Read the sentence from the article.

> **Women and African Americans faced other obstacles, such as unfair treatment, that prevented them from joining.**

What does the word *obstacles* mean in the sentence above?

Ⓐ fees   Ⓒ long lines

Ⓑ problems   Ⓓ written tests

14 Read this sentence from the article.

> **The government even controlled women's clothing to force conservation of products needed by the military.**

The word *conservation* includes the Latin root *serv*, meaning "to keep or guard." What does the word *conservation* mean?

Ⓕ the act of saving

Ⓖ the act of keeping away

Ⓗ the act of taking or stealing

Ⓘ the act of blocking or stopping

15 According to the article, the purpose of the Office of War Information was to

Ⓐ keep track of war deaths and injuries.

Ⓑ set up rationing boards throughout the country.

Ⓒ get people to support the war through government programs.

Ⓓ gather information on how government programs were working.

GO ON →

Copyright © The McGraw-Hill Companies, Inc.

16 Why was rubber one of the first things to be rationed?

(F) Used rubber was not useful to anyone.

(G) Americans did not care about getting new tires.

(H) Rubber plants in the United States were not very efficient.

(I) The United States could not get the raw materials to make rubber.

17 The government made rules about women's clothing to

(A) stop women from buying new skirts.

(B) encourage women to sew at home.

(C) reduce the amount of cloth and leather that was used.

(D) make sure that women in the military would be dressed correctly.

18 Which detail supports the author's point that the country faced a serious problem in fighting the war?

(F) No raw materials were available to build weapons.

(G) People at home did not want to support the war effort.

(H) Farms and factories were not producing what they could.

(I) Many people were not able to work on farms and in factories.

19 Read this sentence from the article.

For most of the war, people had to use one of the 8,000 ration boards, or offices, that sprouted up around the country.

Sprouted up means

(A) added.

(C) needed.

(B) appeared.

(D) separated.

GO ON →

Benchmark Assessment • Benchmark 2

Copyright © The McGraw-Hill Companies, Inc.

20 Read this sentence from the article.

Many people treated their ration books like gold.

Why does the author compare ration books with gold?

Ⓕ Ration books were the same color as gold.

Ⓖ It was easy to get both ration books and gold.

Ⓗ Both ration books and gold were very valuable to people.

Ⓘ You could only get ration books and gold from the government.

21 Which of these statements is supported by both the text and the chart?

Ⓐ Rationing started before the war began.

Ⓑ Rationing for all products was only temporary.

Ⓒ Rationing was not really necessary to win the war.

Ⓓ Rationing covered nearly everything people bought.

22 What information can you find using the chart on rationing?

Ⓕ amount of each good that was rationed

Ⓖ organizations that managed rationing

Ⓗ period of time certain goods were rationed

Ⓘ beginning and end dates of rationing for certain goods

Copyright © The McGraw-Hill Companies, Inc.

GO ON →

Read the passage "Staying in Touch" before answering Numbers 23 through 34.

Staying in Touch

As Abby approached the front door of the nursing home, she felt very beaten down. When she had started volunteering a few months ago, she had had high hopes. She had remembered her grandmother before she died and thought about how important it had been to her every time Abby visited. It was hard to find the time, but now she came two mornings a week when she did not have college classes.

Lately, it had been harder. She felt she was not making much of a difference to anyone. She moved patients around by pushing their wheelchairs and helped out during lunch. Sometimes she led the exercise class, chanting "One, two, one, two," slowly to the music as a small group seated in chairs or wheelchairs raised their arms above their heads.

However, she put on a happy face and greeted Nathan, who always sat by the door. Later, she went to the community room to take her 15-minute break and opened her phone to check for voice or text messages. Then she checked her social sites to see what was happening with her friends and family. She was totally focused on a message from her brother when Greta rolled her wheelchair almost on top of her.

"What are you doing?" Greta demanded. She was always a little pushy, but Abby liked her. Abby wondered sometimes if Greta was loud just to make sure people would listen to her.

"Checking up on my brother. He's doing some sort of research project in New Zealand."

"You can tell all that just from that little thing in your hand?" She shook her head; it was hard for her to comprehend.

"Sure, I get to read whatever he feels like writing, he answers questions I send him, and he can send me pictures, too, even movies."

"I wish I could do that," said Greta. Abby sensed a little sadness in her voice.

GO ON →

Copyright © The McGraw-Hill Companies, Inc.

"Whom would you check up on?"

Greta looked out the window for a moment as she thought about how to answer. Finally, she turned toward Abby. "My children are wonderful," she said, "but they're too far away. One son is on the East coast, one's on the West coast, and my little girl is in Texas." She caught herself and added, "She's not really a little girl, though, since she turned 33 last month."

"How often do you hear from them?"

"They come to visit, but only about once a year. We tried to make a schedule to talk on the phone, but the time difference makes it so we can only talk really early in the morning before I'm awake, or late at night when I'm already asleep. It's hard . . . ." Her voice trailed off, and she turned her wheelchair away from Abby.

Before she left that day, Abby stopped in to see her supervisor, Mrs. Hanson. "What do you think about getting a computer for the community room?" asked Abby.

"A computer? What for?"

"So the residents could e-mail their relatives."

"E-mail? Most of them hardly use the telephone. They'd be afraid to use a computer."

"I'm not sure that's true. I think there are a few who would love it."

Mrs. Hanson frowned and looked skeptical. Finally, she said, "You've got a laptop, right? Why don't you see if you can get some of them interested in using your computer? If there's enough interest, we could try to get a computer for everyone to use."

Abby put up signs on her next day at the home.

Computer Class	10:00 A.M. Thursday	Bring e-mail addresses

GO ON →

Copyright © The McGraw-Hill Companies, Inc.

That first Thursday, Abby found Greta and her friend Susan waiting for her. As Abby opened up her laptop, Susan blurted out, "I only came because Greta made me!"

"Stop being a baby," growled Greta. "You're always talking about staying in touch with your grandkids. Abby's going to teach us how."

Abby set her laptop on a table and slowly walked them through setting up an e-mail account. They followed along, but when it was Greta's turn to enter information, she began rubbing her twisted fingers. "My fingers just don't work very well anymore."

Abby moved to her side and gave her a pencil with the eraser end down. "Here, use this. It will work just as well."

Greta soon created an account and sent several short e-mail messages. Susan watched Greta like a hawk and then did the same, although she used her fingers to type. To their surprise, each of them got a response within a few minutes.

The next Thursday, Greta and Susan were waiting at the front of a line with two other women and a man leaning against the wall. The week after that, the line stretched down the hall.

During that morning session, Mrs. Hanson interrupted Abby as she taught another resident the basics. "Our community computer is coming next week, but it looks like we'll have to make some rules about time limits. So many residents will want to use it!"

Abby just smiled. For Greta, Susan, and many of the others, e-mail was just the beginning. Wait until they hit the senior chat rooms and social sites, she thought. There was a whole new world waiting for them.

Copyright © The McGraw-Hill Companies, Inc.

GO ON →

Now answer Numbers 23 through 34. Base your answers on "Staying in Touch."

(23) Read this sentence from the passage.

> **She was totally focused on a message from her brother when Greta rolled her wheelchair almost on top of her.**

Which word has almost the same meaning as the word *focused*?

(A) built

(B) turned

(C) decided

(D) concentrated

(24) Read this sentence from the passage.

> **She shook her head; it was hard for her to comprehend.**

The word *comprehend* has two Latin roots: *com*, meaning "together" or "common," and *prehendere*, meaning "to take hold of." What does *comprehend* mean?

(F) catch with the hands

(G) pay attention to details

(H) take a risk or chance; dare

(I) grasp with the mind; understand

Copyright © The McGraw-Hill Companies, Inc.

GO ON →

25 Mrs. Hanson is not sure at first about getting a computer for the residents because she thinks that

Ⓐ few residents have relatives to contact.

Ⓑ many residents would not want to use it.

Ⓒ some residents would not take care of it.

Ⓓ many residents would complain about the cost of buying one.

26 Based on what you read, what will Abby most likely do next?

Ⓕ help Greta move into an apartment by herself

Ⓖ quit going to college so she can work at the nursing home

Ⓗ teach the nursing home residents more about using computers

Ⓘ stop volunteering at the nursing home and work with young children instead

27 How does Abby change from the beginning of the passage to the end?

Ⓐ feels at first like she is not doing much, but finally feels good about her efforts

Ⓑ thinks about quitting her job at the nursing home, but at the end decides to stay

Ⓒ is friendly at first with only a few people, but finally makes a lot more friends

Ⓓ feels like the residents do not really appreciate her, but at the end realizes they do

Copyright © The McGraw-Hill Companies, Inc.

GO ON →

28 Which statement best expresses the theme of the passage?

(F) Seniors are able to use computers very effectively.

(G) Families need to visit relatives in nursing homes.

(H) Nursing homes should set up recreation programs for their residents.

(I) People can use their skills to provide new opportunities for others.

29 Read this sentence from the passage.

As Abby approached the front door of the nursing home, she felt very beaten down.

What does this sentence tell you about Abby?

(A) She is excited.

(B) She is hopeful.

(C) She is curious.

(D) She is discouraged.

30 Read these sentences from the passage.

Before [Susan] knew it, Greta had created an account and sent several short e-mail messages. Susan watched Greta like a hawk and then did the same, although she used her fingers to type.

The author compares Susan to a hawk to show that Susan

(F) looked a little like a hawk.

(G) was stronger than Greta.

(H) watched very carefully.

(I) was angry with Greta.

Copyright © The McGraw-Hill Companies, Inc.

GO ON →

31 Which event happens last in the passage?

Ⓐ Greta learns how to use e-mail.

Ⓑ Abby brings her laptop to work.

Ⓒ Greta tells Abby about her family.

Ⓓ Mrs. Hanson agrees to get a computer.

32 How is the setting important to the story?

Ⓕ Seniors in the nursing home are living without their families.

Ⓖ Teens visiting the nursing home do not feel very comfortable.

Ⓗ The nursing home does not have enough workers on its staff.

Ⓘ Little money is available to effectively run the nursing home.

33 How does Abby feel about the residents at the nursing home?

Ⓐ She wishes more of them lived at home.

Ⓑ She likes them and wants to help them.

Ⓒ She thinks they should get better medical care.

Ⓓ She does not understand why they do not get out more.

34 Which of these statements would the narrator most likely agree with?

Ⓕ Young volunteers find that helping seniors is difficult.

Ⓖ Seniors have a lot more interests than people might guess.

Ⓗ Nursing homes need to do a lot more for their residents.

Ⓘ Seniors would rather write letters than type e-mails.

Copyright © The McGraw-Hill Companies, Inc.

GO ON →

Read the article "Living and Working in Space" before answering Numbers 35 through 44.

Living and Working in Space

More than 200 miles above the earth's surface, a Russian spacecraft connected to the International Space Station, or ISS, just before Christmas in 2011. It brought three new crew members who came from the United States, the Netherlands, and Russia. They joined three already there, and all systems were go.

Dutch astronaut Andre Kuipers was ready to begin his second visit to the ISS. He had spent 11 days there in 2004. This time he would stay nearly five months. "It feels like going back home, but the house will have doubled its size since my last visit," said Kuipers before he took off. The living and working space inside the ISS is now about as big as a five-bedroom house. It has two bathrooms and a gymnasium.

The ISS weighs almost a million pounds. It stretches out over an area as large as a football field, including the end zones! There is no rocket powerful enough to carry it into space. Smaller rockets brought the astronauts and pieces of the space station into orbit. Then the astronauts put the pieces together as they sailed around the world at more than 17,000 miles per hour.

Building in Space

Since November 2, 2000, more than 200 people have stayed on the ISS. They have constantly expanded their home. The first section of the station was only about 42 feet long and 14 feet wide. Regular trips back and forth to the ISS brought supplies and new sections that the astronauts attached to the existing station. Some work was done with a bending metal arm 55 feet long. It could lift about 220,000 pounds. The astronauts controlled it from inside the station.

In most cases, the astronauts also had to become construction workers. They dressed in special space suits that controlled the temperature and pressure. When they left the station, they floated in outer space. They were attached by two long cords, so that if there was a problem with one cord, the other would keep them from floating away.

GO ON →

Copyright © The McGraw-Hill Companies, Inc.

They used hand and power tools to put the pieces in the proper positions. Then they had to tighten the nuts and bolts that hold the station together. Sometimes they worked as long as seven hours outside of the station.

A Flying Laboratory

During the earlier years, much of the astronauts' time was eaten up by construction. But many hands make light work. Now, because most of the planned station is completed, they have more time for scientific experiments. One of the reasons for building the ISS was to find out more about outer space and how humans react to it.

Andre Kuipers is a medical doctor who planned to perform experiments about 40 hours per week. Some were observations about his own body. He would record information about how his body changes because he is living without gravity, called weightlessness. Scientists can use the information as people prepare for even longer space flights. Some day, people may take a seven-month trip to Mars.

He planned to conduct about 20 other experiments for other countries in the Columbus Laboratory on the ISS. It is a section built by various European countries. The laboratory was attached in 2008.

Countries Working Together

Some people have questioned how useful the ISS has been. It has cost the United States over $100 billion. The total cost for all countries is over $150 billion. Scientists have made a lot of progress by building the ISS and doing experiments there. But there might have been even more progress if the same amount of money had been spent on scientific research on Earth.

The greatest achievement of the ISS may not be related to research. It is the first time in history so many countries have cooperated on such a complex and expensive project. In the 1940s, Japan and the United States fought a terrible war against each other that resulted in millions of deaths and injuries. Not long after that, the United States and its allies in Europe faced the Soviet Union (Russia) in a bitter rivalry around the world. Now, these countries are working together in exploring space.

Copyright © The McGraw-Hill Companies, Inc.

GO ON →

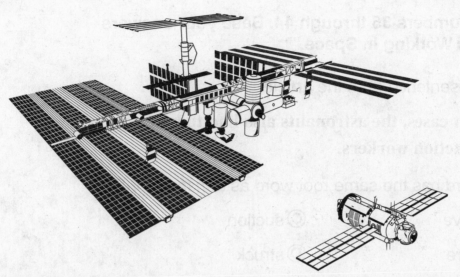

The model (left) shows the small size of the first ISS module, or unit. Today, the much larger ISS (right) is about the size of a football field.

The effort that created the ISS began about 1993. The United States and Russia were the first countries involved. They were later joined by Canada, Japan, and various European countries. Today, money, workers, and equipment from 22 countries participate in the project. ISS member countries prepare schedules together and agree on technical ideas years in advance. This work has been successful even though citizens of member countries speak different languages, have different types of government, and use different forms of money.

For the Dutch astronaut Andre Kuipers, the space station is a home away from home. The astronauts from the United States, Russia, and other countries also think of it in the same way. The space station is a scientific home for people from around the world. Just a few years ago, the same people may have raised weapons against each other, but now they are sharing scientific observations.

Copyright © The McGraw-Hill Companies, Inc.

ISS Timeline

First module launched from Russia; first new section attached by U.S.	ISS becomes a "construction site" as many new sections are attached.	Full crew of 6 stays on ISS after new sections attached.

1993   1998   2000   2002   2004   2009   2010

Russia and U.S. agree to work together on space projects.	First crew stays on ISS for lengthy time; regular supply flights begin.	U.S. decides to end funding for ISS after 2016.	U.S. renews support for ISS until 2020.

GO ON →

Now answer Numbers 35 through 44. Base your answers on "Living and Working in Space."

35 Read this sentence from the article.

> **In most cases, the astronauts also had to become construction workers.**

Which word has the same root word as *construction*?

Ⓐ conserve   Ⓒ suction

Ⓑ structure   Ⓓ struck

36 Read this sentence from the article.

> **The living and working space inside the ISS is now about as big as a five-bedroom house.**

Which meaning of the word *space* is the same one used in the sentence above?

Ⓕ vast region above the Earth's atmosphere

Ⓖ put distance between objects and people

Ⓗ period of time from one event to another

Ⓘ area set aside for a particular purpose

37 What is the main idea of the section "Building in Space"?

Ⓐ Many countries designed the ISS, but only a few paid for it.

Ⓑ Many astronauts have helped expand the ISS to its current size.

Ⓒ The astronauts wanted to have more time to perform experiments.

Ⓓ The ISS is too big of a structure to be built on the surface of the Earth.

Copyright © The McGraw-Hill Companies, Inc.

GO ON →

38 Based on the information in the article, how does the author most likely feel about the level of international support for the ISS?

Ⓕ All participating countries will want to use the ISS for the rest of the century.

Ⓖ The number of countries using the ISS will increase greatly in the near future.

Ⓗ Not everyone agrees that we should spend billions of dollars on the ISS project.

Ⓘ Many new countries probably want to put their own astronauts on board the ISS.

39 What information in the article supports the idea that Andre Kuipers was looking forward to his second stay on the ISS?

Ⓐ He compares it to going home.

Ⓑ He was supposed to stay for almost five months.

Ⓒ He planned to observe the reactions of his own body.

Ⓓ He helped increase the size of the crew to six members.

40 Read these sentences from the article.

> **It brought three new crew members who came from the United States, the Netherlands, and Russia. They joined three already there, and all systems were go.**

The phrase *all systems were go* means

Ⓕ into space.

Ⓖ equal in number.

Ⓗ beyond a maximum limit.

Ⓘ everything is ready to begin.

Copyright © The McGraw-Hill Companies, Inc.

GO ON →

Name: _____ **Date:** _____

41 Read these sentences from the article.

> **During the earlier years, much of the astronauts' time was eaten up by construction. But many hands make light work.**

What does "But many hands make light work" mean?

Ⓐ More help eases the job.   Ⓒ People need work.

Ⓑ Workers are needed.   Ⓓ Nothing gets done.

42 Read this sentence from the article.

> **For the Dutch astronaut Andre Kuipers, the space station is a home away from home.**

What does the phrase "home away from home" mean?

Ⓕ The ISS is about the size of Kuipers' home.

Ⓖ Kuipers wanted to decorate the inside of the ISS.

Ⓗ The ISS is a comfortable place for Kuipers.

Ⓘ Kuipers wanted to be home for Christmas.

43 What information is in the timeline that is not in the article?

Ⓐ The ISS gets regular supply flights.

Ⓑ The full crew of the ISS is six astronauts.

Ⓒ The U.S. considered ending the funding for the ISS.

Ⓓ The U.S. and Russia were the first countries in the ISS.

44 What does the illustration show?

Ⓕ The ISS was built in space.

Ⓖ Solar panels power the ISS.

Ⓗ The Columbus Laboratory was added in 2008.

Ⓘ The current ISS is much bigger than the original unit.

Copyright © The McGraw-Hill Companies, Inc.

GO ON →

Read the article "A Remarkable Scientist" before answering Numbers 45 through 53.

A Remarkable Scientist

During World War I in France, many soldiers died because they did not get good medical care. Doctors at the time did not know about many procedures and medicines that could have saved lives. It was also very hard to get the best medical equipment to the areas where soldiers were wounded. However, that situation began to change. A brand-new medical technique called the x-ray was invented, and a scientist was able to bring the invention to the battlefield. Today, the x-ray is still the primary tool that doctors use to find broken bones and other problems.

Marie Curie was 47 years old at the time. She was a famous scientist who had been sent away from Paris for her own protection during the war. But she realized that the research she was doing at the time could help save lives—and she kept at it.

First, she persuaded some automakers to turn some cars into vans so she could carry x-ray equipment in them. Then she trained her 17-year-old daughter Irene to use the new equipment and brought her along. They lived the hard life of soldiers near the fighting and trained others to do the same work.

Their x-ray vans were easy to recognize and decorated with a red cross. The vans were so familiar to soldiers that they began to call them *petites Curies*, or "little Curies." By the end of the war, Marie and her daughter had developed over 200 x-ray units. They had supervised over a million x-rays.

Helping an Adopted Country

One thing that made her work so special to the people of France was that Marie Curie had been born and raised in the city of Warsaw in Poland. Her parents were teachers, and she had been an outstanding student her entire life. Much of Poland was controlled by Russia at the time, and she and her father supported a movement to free the country from Russia. She soon realized that to get a full university education, she would have to leave Warsaw.

GO ON →

Copyright © The McGraw-Hill Companies, Inc.

First, Marie worked to support her older sister who moved to Paris to get medical training. Then her sister did the same for Marie when Marie came to study physics in Paris in 1891.

Marie had just enough money to pay for college, a tiny attic apartment, and very little food. Even though she was often sick during this period, she completed her work in only three years. Because Marie was a top student, she got a scholarship to continue her work. Soon after that, the world sat up and took notice.

In 1894, Marie began to do research in a small lab run by Pierre Curie. They married the next year and began to work together on research. Marie persuaded Pierre to help her finish the work required to get the highest degree in physics. She became the first woman in the world to earn a doctor's degree in science.

Rising Stars

Once Marie and Pierre married, their work grew and their fame took off. Marie convinced Pierre they should work on a new discovery by German and French scientists. They had discovered that some substances gave off rays that could pass through wood or human skin. Marie was the first to call this *radioactivity*.

Soon, the Curies discovered a new element that was radioactive. Marie named it *polonium* to honor the country of Poland where she grew up. After discovering another new radioactive element, they were awarded the Nobel Prize in Physics in 1903. The Nobel Prize is the highest award in the world for scientific discoveries.

Pierre was given a good teaching job at the best college in France. Marie was able to do research in a good laboratory. They had two daughters, and Pierre's father helped care for them.

A Sudden Turn

In 1906, Pierre Curie stepped off a curb on a rainy night in Paris directly in front of a wagon pulled by horses. He was immediately trampled to death. Not long afterward, Pierre's father became sick and died also.

Copyright © The McGraw-Hill Companies, Inc.

GO ON →

Marie's world was suddenly turned upside down, but she continued her work. She was so successful that she was awarded a second Nobel Prize, this time in chemistry. She was the first person to receive two Nobel Prizes. She is still the only person in history to receive them in two different sciences.

Deadly Effects

The Curies' research paved the way for many later discoveries. But what the Curies did not realize at the time was that radioactive substances can be very harmful. They handled radioactive materials without any protection.

The materials were fascinating. They gave off a faint, blue glow and were actually warm to the touch. Marie Curie was exposed to their harmful rays for many years before people realized their danger. Because she absorbed so much radioactivity, even the objects around her were affected. Today, her cookbook has to be stored in a protective case so that people are not harmed by the radioactivity.

Marie Curie died in 1934 from the effects of harmful radiation. During World War I, she had written, "I am resolved to put all my strength at the service of my adopted country." She had put all of her strength into gaining scientific knowledge as well. She remains one of the most respected and honored scientists in history.

Copyright © The McGraw-Hill Companies, Inc.

GO ON →

Now answer Numbers 45 through 53. Base your answers on the article "A Remarkable Scientist."

45 Read these sentences from the article.

> **A brand-new medical technique called the x-ray was invented, and a scientist was able to bring the invention to the battlefield. Today, the x-ray is still the primary tool that doctors use to find broken bones and other problems.**

What is the meaning of *primary* as it is used above?

Ⓐ final

Ⓑ fastest

Ⓒ most expensive

Ⓓ most important

46 Read this sentence from the article.

> **First, she persuaded some automakers to turn some cars into vans so she could carry x-ray equipment in them.**

Which word has about the same meaning as the word *persuaded* as used in the sentence above?

Ⓕ allowed

Ⓖ convinced

Ⓗ discouraged

Ⓘ prevented

47 The author organized the first section of the article by

Ⓐ pointing out the causes and effects of World War I.

Ⓑ comparing and contrasting the work of different scientists.

Ⓒ stating the order of importance of various scientific discoveries.

Ⓓ showing the problem and the solution of getting medical help to soldiers.

GO ON →

Copyright © The McGraw-Hill Companies, Inc.

48 Which of these events happened after Pierre Curie's death?

Ⓕ Marie Curie moved from Warsaw to Paris.

Ⓖ Marie Curie was awarded her first Nobel prize.

Ⓗ Marie Curie was the first to name *radioactivity*.

Ⓘ Marie and Irene Curie used x-rays on soldiers.

49 According to the article, what was the cause of Marie Curie's death?

Ⓐ living like a soldier during World War I

Ⓑ sadness over the death of Pierre Curie and his father

Ⓒ exhaustion from many years of hard work as a research scientist

Ⓓ handling radioactive materials for many years without protection

50 Read these sentences from the article.

Because Marie was a top student, she got a scholarship to continue her work. Soon after that, the world sat up and took notice.

What does these sentences mean?

Ⓕ Some people in the world sat and watched Marie Curie work.

Ⓖ Marie Curie soon impressed many people with her work.

Ⓗ Soon after Marie started work, people gathered to watch her.

Ⓘ Marie Curie greatly changed the way the world carried out work.

Copyright © The McGraw-Hill Companies, Inc.

GO ON →

51 Read this sentence from the article.

> **Once Marie and Pierre married, their work grew and their fame took off.**

This sentence shows that Marie and Pierre

Ⓐ disappeared.

Ⓑ became widely known.

Ⓒ caused many problems.

Ⓓ traveled a long distance.

52 Read this sentence from the article.

> **The Curies' research paved the way for many later discoveries.**

What does the phrase "paved the way for many later discoveries" mean as it is used in the sentence above?

Ⓕ helped scientists travel farther to do research

Ⓖ raised money for later discoveries

Ⓗ made later discoveries possible

Ⓘ prevented many mistakes

53 Which section of the article provides the best information on how Marie Curie came to live in France?

Ⓐ Helping an Adopted Country

Ⓑ Rising Stars

Ⓒ A Sudden Turn

Ⓓ Deadly Effects

Copyright © The McGraw-Hill Companies, Inc.

GO ON →

Read the letter "Greetings from the South Pole" before answering Numbers 54 through 60.

Greetings from the South Pole

December 20

Dear Mom, Dad, and Little Sister,

Greetings from the South Pole! I know we've already exchanged lots of quick e-mails, but I thought I'd sit down and write a real letter. In this way, I can make sure I let people know about some things here at McMurdo Station. (I've enclosed a picture.) We're not actually at the South Pole; we're about 850 miles north of it.

It's the middle of summer here, but it's almost Christmas. The sun shines all day and night. I'm finally getting used to it, although there are times I just wish it was dark outside. The only way to sleep is to keep the heavy curtains closed tightly.

Do you realize that there are days when it's warmer here than it is at home? Some days it gets above 40 degrees, and the average is around 20. However, it does get really cold in the summer when the wind howls down from the Transantarctic Mountains across the waters of McMurdo Sound. This is nothing like the winter when the sun never rises. They say it's like midnight all the time. The temperature in June can get as low as 50 degrees below zero with winds of more than 100 miles per hour. You're taking your life in your hands if you go out unprepared.

It's nice to be able to go outside here in the summer, but there are only a couple of trails we can go on unless it's a special trip. It's too dangerous otherwise. There are about 1,000 people here doing research and taking care of the buildings, rooms, and meals. It doesn't make sense to let people just wander off on their own.

Copyright © The McGraw-Hill Companies, Inc.

GO ON →

Dad, I know how much you love to hike so you'd probably go nuts here. The longest of the hikes is about 2 miles, but it is very beautiful. The glaciers have ice in them that's several thousand years old, and it glitters like a million diamonds when the sun is at just the right angle. You'd love the surprise of seeing the flocks of big South Polar sea birds, too. They're called skuas, and they only come during the warmest months. Mostly they're looking for a good meal from whatever food scraps they can find.

Mom, I'm sure you're worried about your little girl (even though I'm almost 30) stranded here at the South Pole surrounded by so many men. But there have been women working here for more than 30 years. There are still more men than women, but the numbers are getting closer.

There's one thing you wouldn't like, which is hard for me, too. Most days I'm alone for only a few minutes! Nearly everyone shares rooms like in college, and we eat our meals together in the cafeteria. I have two regular roommates, and the fourth bed in our room is used by women who are just passing through on their way somewhere else. We share a bathroom and shower, and men have rooms across the hall. There is not much privacy.

But we work hard six days a week, and nearly everyone enjoys the work. We all volunteered to be here because it's a chance to find out things that we could not learn anywhere else. We feel lucky to be chosen by the National Science Foundation. Most of us believe that our work here can help people save the environment. As you know, I am working on measuring changes in the size of the ice covering Antarctica. If everyone knows that the ice is actually melting, maybe we can stop Earth from heating up so much.

I think about you a lot, Christina. (I know I should not keep calling you Little Sister, but it's a habit I've had for a long time.) Too bad you couldn't come down here for New Year's Day. For years, they've had a large outdoor party that goes on all day long.

Copyright © The McGraw-Hill Companies, Inc.

GO ON →

They call it Ice Stock. (There was a famous music festival years ago called Woodstock. You can ask Mom and Dad about it.) People here play loud music or recordings, there's a chili cook-off, and everyone spends the day celebrating and relaxing.

Well, it's getting late, although you could not deduce that by looking outside. It's still as bright as noon! Anyway, I'll conclude with one of the memories I could never get anywhere else in the world.

One day I ended up with some other researchers who were tracking changes in the penguin population. As they moved around among 1,000 Adelie penguins, the penguins made an awful sound. It wasn't anything like what I imagined friendly, cuddly penguins might make. Together, they made a noise that sounded like a giant car engine trying to start. I was told that they keep this up for hours. I did not like the noise, but I'm glad I corrected my imagination with real facts. I guess that's why I'm a scientist.

Much love to all of you. I'll see you in a few months.

Sincerely,

Vanessa

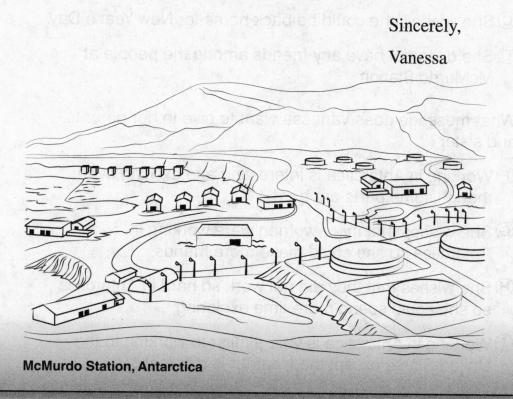

McMurdo Station, Antarctica

Copyright © The McGraw-Hill Companies, Inc.

GO ON →

Now answer Numbers 54 through 60. Base your answers on "Greetings from the South Pole."

54 Read these sentences from the article.

> **Well, it's getting late, although you could not deduce that by looking outside. It's still as bright as noon!**

What is the meaning of *deduce* as it is used in the sentence above?

F continue working

G waste time

H figure out

I tell a story

55 Based on the letter, what can you conclude about Vanessa?

A She does not plan to get married in the near future.

B She graduated from college and has scientific training.

C She wishes she could be back home for New Year's Day.

D She does not have any friends among the people at McMurdo Station.

56 What message does Vanessa want to give to her parents and sister?

F Working in Antarctica is interesting and exciting even though some parts are hard.

G She wishes that more women were working in Antarctica so she could make more friends.

H She wishes that they did not work so hard in Antarctica so she could spend more time exploring.

I Working in Antarctica is very similar to working in the United States except the weather is different.

Copyright © The McGraw-Hill Companies, Inc.

GO ON →

57 What information about Vanessa does the reader get in the second paragraph of the letter?

Ⓐ She does not like sleeping during the day.

Ⓑ She loves the idea that the sun never sets.

Ⓒ It has taken a while for her to adjust to living in Antarctica.

Ⓓ She doesn't like celebrating holidays in the middle of the summer.

58 What does Vanessa think about her work in Antarctica?

Ⓕ She would rather work alone than work with a large group.

Ⓖ She is proud of her work and thinks it will make a difference in the world.

Ⓗ She wishes that she could study the penguins instead of observing the ice.

Ⓘ She does not like working six days a week because she does not have enough time to go hiking.

59 What does Vanessa learn from her experience with the penguins?

Ⓐ She really enjoys being away from the camp and working outside.

Ⓑ What she imagines about things isn't always true.

Ⓒ The number of penguins is dropping each year.

Ⓓ Being surrounded by penguins isn't much fun.

60 How are Vanessa and her mother alike?

Ⓕ They both think Christina should study more.

Ⓖ They both think more women should be scientists.

Ⓗ They both like to spend some time alone.

Ⓘ They both enjoy hiking.

Copyright © The McGraw-Hill Companies, Inc.

Part 2: Writing

Kara made an outline to organize her ideas for a paper. Use her plan to answer questions 1–4.

Kara's Writing Plan

I. Greek Gods

    A. Zeus

        1. chief god

        2. ruler of the sky

    B. Apollo

        1. god of the sun

        2. the healer

    C. Greek city-states

        1. Athens

        2. Sparta

    D. Poseidon

        1. ruler of the sea

        2. giver of horses

Copyright © The McGraw-Hill Companies, Inc.

GO ON →

1 Which entry is off topic and should be removed from the outline?

(A) Zeus

(B) Apollo

(C) Greek city-states

(D) Poseidon

2 Which note below is on topic and should be added to the outline?

(F) Olympus—home of the gods

(G) Ares—the god of war

(H) The Trojan War—stories

(I) Ancient Egypt—gods and goddesses

3 Which note below is on topic and should be added to the outline?

(A) Hermes—the messenger god

(B) Homer—a storyteller

(C) Dragons—monsters

(D) Aegean Sea—sailing ships

4 Based on the information in Kara's Writing Plan, what kind of paper is she planning to write?

(F) a paper that tells a myth explaining how the sun rises and sets

(G) a paper that compares the gods and goddesses of different lands

(H) a paper that gives information about the gods of ancient Greece

(I) a paper that convinces readers to read Greek myths

Copyright © The McGraw-Hill Companies, Inc.

GO ON →

The book report below is a first draft that Mark wrote. It contains mistakes. Read the book report to answer questions 5 through 11.

(1) Jaclyn Rose's latest book is *Kind Angel of the Battlefield*. (2) It tells the story of Clara Barton, who founded the American Red Cross.

(3) Clara Barton had an interesting life. (4) Born in 1821, she was the youngest of five children. (5) In her first job, Clara Barton was a teacher. (6) Later, she set up her own school!

(7) The Civil War started in 1861. (8) Soon, Clara Barton was helping soldiers. (9) She risked her life bringing supplies to troops and tending wounded soldiers. (10) She set up field hospitals. (11) Because she was so kind, soldiers called Clara Barton the "Angel of the Battlefield."

(12) After the Civil War, Clara Barton continues her work with relief organizations. (13) She helped to found the American Red Cross. (14) Soon, the Red Cross expanded her mission. (15) The organization began to help victims of floods, fires, and other natural disasters. (16) The Red Cross continues this work today.

(17) I believe that everybody should read Jaclyn Rose's book.

Copyright © The McGraw-Hill Companies, Inc.

GO ON →

5 What is the simple subject of sentence 1?

Ⓐ Jaclyn Rose's latest book

Ⓑ Jaclyn Rose

Ⓒ is

Ⓓ book

6 Which word in sentence 5 is a noun in a prepositional phrase?

Ⓕ first

Ⓖ job

Ⓗ Clara Barton

Ⓘ teacher

7 Which sentence contains a dependent clause?

Ⓐ Sentence 8

Ⓑ Sentence 9

Ⓒ Sentence 10

Ⓓ Sentence 11

8 Which word in sentence 9 is an adjective that modifies a noun?

Ⓕ her

Ⓖ bringing

Ⓗ tending

Ⓘ wounded

Copyright © The McGraw-Hill Companies, Inc.

GO ON →

9 What is the correct way to write sentence 12?

Ⓐ After the Civil War, Clara Barton continues her work with relief organizations.

Ⓑ After the Civil War, Clara Barton continued her work with relief organizations.

Ⓒ After the Civil War, Clara Barton was continuing her work with relief organizations.

Ⓓ After the Civil War, Clara Barton had continued her work with relief organizations.

10 How can sentence 14 best be written?

Ⓕ Soon, the Red Cross expanded its mission.

Ⓖ Soon, the Red Cross expanded his mission.

Ⓗ Soon, the Red Cross expanded their mission.

Ⓘ Soon, the Red Cross expanded our mission.

11 Which sentence contains a prepositional phrase that serves as an adjective?

Ⓐ Sentence 13

Ⓑ Sentence 14

Ⓒ Sentence 15

Ⓓ Sentence 16

Copyright © The McGraw-Hill Companies, Inc.

GO ON →

Read this passage about a new memorial to Martin Luther King, Jr. Choose the word or words that correctly complete questions 12–18.

The Martin Luther King, Jr. Memorial

The Martin Luther King, Jr. Memorial opened in 2011. Martin Luther King, Jr. __(12)__ for the rights of African Americans. __(13)__ always favored nonviolent methods of protest. The memorial honors this great civil rights leader. It __(14)__ on the National Mall in Washington, D.C., near other famous American monuments.

A towering sculpture of Dr. King greets all visitors. A granite inscription wall winds around the memorial. The wall contains quotations from many of __(15)__ most famous speeches.

Nature plays a role in the memorial, too. Every year, cherry trees __(16)__ at the memorial near the anniversary of Dr. King's assassination. Elm and myrtle trees also grow __(17)__ . The sight and sound of flowing water give a feeling of peace. The new memorial is __(18)__ a museum nor a shrine; it is a beautiful living space and an appropriate honor to a great man.

Copyright © The McGraw-Hill Companies, Inc.

GO ON →

12 Which answer should go in blank (12)?

Ⓕ fight

Ⓖ fought

Ⓗ fighting

13 Which answer should go in blank (13)?

Ⓐ He

Ⓑ We

Ⓒ They

14 Which answer should go in blank (14)?

Ⓕ located

Ⓖ was locating

Ⓗ is located

15 Which answer should go in blank (15)?

Ⓐ him

Ⓑ his

Ⓒ their

Copyright © The McGraw-Hill Companies, Inc.

GO ON →

16 Which answer should go in blank (16)?

   Ⓕ bloom

   Ⓖ bloomed

   Ⓗ blooming

17 Which answer should go in blank (17)?

   Ⓐ they're

   Ⓑ their

   Ⓒ there

18 Which answer should go in blank (18)?

   Ⓕ both

   Ⓖ neither

   Ⓗ or

Copyright © The McGraw-Hill Companies, Inc.

GO ON →

The passage below is a draft that Ginny wrote. It contains mistakes. Read the passage to answer questions 19 through 26.

(1) It was Thanksgiving morning but Lisa and her parents were not fixing dinner for their family. (2) They were getting ready to serve a meal to residents of nearby Senior House.

(3) Lisa and her parents loaded bags with homemade bread. (4) They also carried out some big containers of coleslaw to their car. (5) "Time to go," Lisa's mother said.

(6) The kitchen at Senior House was full of volunteers. (7) The huge dining area smelled wonderful. (8) Lisa and her parents helped to set up tables. (9) They put out bowls of coleslaw and platters of bread.

(10) When the residents arrived at the dining area volunteers quickly served a tasty meal. (11) They brought out heaping plates of turkey, potatoes, and gravy for everyone. (12) The residents thanked them for the wonderful feast.

(13) After they served the meal, the volunteers cleaned up. (14) Then they left for home. (15) Lisa felt tired. (16) She also felt happy. (17) She could not have imagined a better way to celebrate Thanksgiving Day than by helping others.

Copyright © The McGraw-Hill Companies, Inc.

GO ON →

19 How can sentence 1 best be written?

(A) It was Thanksgiving morning; but Lisa and her parents were not fixing dinner for their family.

(B) It was Thanksgiving morning, but Lisa and her parents were not fixing dinner for their family.

(C) It was Thanksgiving morning, so Lisa and her parents were not fixing dinner for their family.

(D) It was Thanksgiving morning; so Lisa and her parents were not fixing dinner for their family.

20 Which word from sentence 3 is a noun in a prepositional phrase?

(F) Lisa

(G) parents

(H) bags

(I) bread

21 Which word in sentence 4 is a possessive pronoun?

(A) they   (C) big

(B) some   (D) their

22 How can sentence 10 best be written?

(F) At the dining area, volunteers when the residents arrived served a tasty meal.

(G) The residents arrived at the dining area, volunteers quickly served a tasty meal.

(H) When the residents arrived at the dining area; volunteers quickly served a tasty meal.

(I) When the residents arrived at the dining area, volunteers quickly served a tasty meal.

Copyright © The McGraw-Hill Companies, Inc.

GO ON →

23 Which word in Sentence 11 is an adjective?

Ⓐ heaping

Ⓑ plates

Ⓒ turkey

Ⓓ everyone

24 Which of these is a complex sentence?

Ⓕ Sentence 12

Ⓖ Sentence 13

Ⓗ Sentence 14

Ⓘ Sentence 15

25 Which is the best way to combine sentences 15 and 16?

Ⓐ Lisa felt tired, she also felt happy.

Ⓑ Lisa felt tired because she also felt happy.

Ⓒ Lisa felt tired, but she also felt happy.

Ⓓ Lisa felt tired, so she also felt happy.

26 What is the main verb in sentence 17?

Ⓕ could

Ⓖ imagined

Ⓗ better

Ⓘ helping

Read the passage below. Choose the word or words that correctly complete questions 27–34.

A peacock is a kind of bird, ____(27)____ is sometimes called a peafowl. Most people ____(28)____ peacocks because of their huge fan of 200 rear feathers. Only males have that beautiful fan. They use their fan to attract females. Male peafowls also have bright blue breasts and necks.

A peacock's fan makes up over 60 percent of ____(29)____ length. Peacocks ____(30)____ long wings, as well. In fact, peacocks are one of the world's largest flying birds.

Female peafowls are called peahens. Peahens ____(31)____ as gorgeous as male peafowls. They are mostly brown on top, white on the bottom.

Peafowls ____(32)____ in India. Peafowls ____(33)____ the national bird of modern India. They are like ____(34)____ bald eagles in the United States. The people of India tell many tales about these famous birds.

Copyright © The McGraw-Hill Companies, Inc.

GO ON →

27 Which answer should go in blank (27)?

Ⓐ who

Ⓑ whom

Ⓒ which

28 Which answer should go in blank (28)?

Ⓕ are recognizing

Ⓖ did recognize

Ⓗ can recognize

29 Which answer should go in blank (29)?

Ⓐ its

Ⓑ it's

Ⓒ its'

30 Which answer should go in blank (30)?

Ⓕ have

Ⓖ had

Ⓗ are having

Copyright © The McGraw-Hill Companies, Inc.

GO ON →

Benchmark Assessment • Benchmark 2

31 Which answer should go in blank (31)?

Ⓐ arn't

Ⓑ aren't

Ⓒ ar'nt

32 Which answer should go in blank (32)?

Ⓕ originate

Ⓖ originates

Ⓗ originated

33 Which answer should go in blank (33)?

Ⓐ have become

Ⓑ becamed

Ⓒ have becomed

34 Which answer should go in blank (34)?

Ⓕ his

Ⓖ our

Ⓗ their

Copyright © The McGraw-Hill Companies, Inc.

The myth below is a first draft that Nick wrote. It contains mistakes. Read the myth to answer questions 35 through 42.

How Did Turtle Get Its Shell?

(1) Long ago, Turtle had no shell. (2) In the summer, Turtle was happy. (3) Turtle worried at the approach of cold weather, though. (4) "I must look for a home today," Turtle said.

(5) Turtle found a tree with many holes. (6) "I will make my home in a hole," he said. (7) Unfortunately, the holes were filled with squirrels and birds. (8) Turtle walked on.

(9) Next, Turtle found a tunnel in the ground. (10) Unfortunately, the twisting tunnel was full of rabbits and chipmunks. (11) Finally, Turtle stopped at a sandbar. (12) There, he decided to dig a hole for shelter. (13) "I will look for a home tomorrow," Turtle said.

(14) Turtle fell asleep under the warm sand. (15) He awoke, Turtle was surprised. (16) The sand and pebbles had hardened into a shell. (17) He could not get out. (18) He was stuck there. (19) Turtle could only poke his head in and out of the shell. (20) "But now I have a home to take with me, wherever I go," Turtle said.

(21) That is how Turtle got its shell.

Copyright © The McGraw-Hill Companies, Inc.

GO ON →

35 What is the complete predicate of sentence 3?

(A) Turtle

(B) worried at

(C) the approach of cold weather

(D) worried at the approach of cold weather, though

36 How can sentences 7 and 8 best be combined?

(F) Unfortunately, the holes were filled with squirrels and birds, Turtle walked on.

(G) Unfortunately, the holes were filled with squirrels and birds, so Turtle walked on.

(H) Unfortunately, the holes were filled with squirrels and birds, but Turtle walked on.

(I) Unfortunately, the holes were filled with squirrels and birds, as a result, Turtle walked on.

37 What is the complete subject of sentence 10?

(A) tunnel

(B) the twisting tunnel

(C) unfortunately, the twisting tunnel

(D) tunnel was full of rabbits and chipmunks

38 What is the best way to combine sentences 11 and 12?

(F) Finally, Turtle stopped at a sandbar, and, there, he decided to dig a hole for shelter.

(G) Finally, Turtle stopped at a sandbar, but, there, he decided to dig a hole for shelter.

(H) Finally, Turtle stopped at a sandbar, where he decided to dig a hole for shelter.

(I) Finally, Turtle stopped at a sandbar, so, there, he decided to dig a hole for shelter.

Copyright © The McGraw-Hill Companies, Inc.

GO ON →

39 Which sentence contains a prepositional phrase that serves as an adverb?

Ⓐ Sentence 14

Ⓑ Sentence 15

Ⓒ Sentence 17

Ⓓ Sentence 18

40 Which is the correct way to change the word order of sentence 15?

Ⓕ He awoke, so Turtle was surprised.

Ⓖ Then Turtle awoke, he was surprised.

Ⓗ When he awoke, Turtle was surprised.

Ⓘ He awoke, or Turtle was surprised.

41 Which word in sentence 16 is a noun in a prepositional phrase?

Ⓐ sand

Ⓑ pebbles

Ⓒ into

Ⓓ shell

42 Which word from sentence 20 is a subordinating conjunction?

Ⓕ now

Ⓖ to

Ⓗ with

Ⓘ wherever

Copyright © The McGraw-Hill Companies, Inc.

GO ON →

Read the story below. Choose the word that correctly completes questions 43–50.

I was walking my dog Lucky after school ___(43)___ a huge rabbit jumped out of a hole by the sidewalk. Lucky immediately charged after the rabbit. I ___(44)___ not hold on to the leash. Lucky chased the rabbit up a street far from ___(45)___ neighborhood. Then he ran into ___(46)___ unfamiliar yard and raced through the door of a strange house.

I hurried to the door and ___(47)___ inside. Everything was upside down. The table, chairs, couches, and stools all hung from the ceiling. Lucky kept on chasing the rabbit around and around that upside-down furniture. They knocked over a lamp and ___(48)___ a vase.

Finally, the rabbit raced out the door. Lucky tried to follow the rabbit, ___(49)___ I grabbed his leash first. ___(50)___ both fell to the ground.

After that . . . I woke up. It was all a weird dream, after all.

Copyright © The McGraw-Hill Companies, Inc.

GO ON →

43 Which answer should go in blank (43)?

Ⓐ where

Ⓑ when

Ⓒ although

44 Which answer should go in blank (44)?

Ⓕ could

Ⓖ must

Ⓗ might

45 Which answer should go in blank (45)?

Ⓐ their

Ⓑ your

Ⓒ our

46 Which answer should go in blank (46)?

Ⓕ an

Ⓖ the

Ⓗ a

GO ON →

Copyright © The McGraw-Hill Companies, Inc.

47 Which answer should go in blank (47)?

Ⓐ peer

Ⓑ was peering

Ⓒ peered

48 Which answer should go in blank (48)?

Ⓕ were broken

Ⓖ break

Ⓗ broke

49 Which answer should go in blank (49)?

Ⓐ and

Ⓑ but

Ⓒ because

50 Which answer should go in blank (50)?

Ⓕ We

Ⓖ Us

Ⓗ I

Copyright © The McGraw-Hill Companies, Inc.

STOP

Writing Prompt – Opinion Letter

The world around us changes over time. People construct new buildings and new roads. Seeds blossom as flowers or trees. Children grow up to become adults.

Some changes are small. Other changes are big and dramatic. Some changes are sudden. Others are slow.

Think of an example of a change that you have seen or learned about in your school, neighborhood, or town. Write an opinion letter telling why you believe that change is for the better or not. Be sure to describe the change clearly. Also, give evidence, or facts, details, or examples, to support your opinion.

Use the space below to plan your writing. Write your final copy on a clean sheet of paper.

_____

_____

_____

_____

_____

_____

_____

_____

_____

Copyright © The McGraw-Hill Companies, Inc.

Question	Correct Answer	Content Focus	CCSS	Complexity
1	B	Context Clues: Multiple-Meaning Words	L.5.4a	DOK 2
2	G	Latin Roots	L.5.4b	DOK 1
3	C	Main Idea and Key Details	RI.5.2	DOK 2
4	I	Main Idea and Key Details	RI.5.1	DOK 3
5	B	Text Structure: Cause and Effect	RI.5.3	DOK 2
6	I	Author's Point of View	RI.5.8	DOK 3
7	D	Personification	L.5.5a	DOK 2
8	H	Simile	L.5.5a	DOK 2
9	D	Idioms	L.5.5b	DOK 2
10	G	Text Features: Maps	RI.4.7	DOK 2
11	B	Antonyms	L.5.5c	DOK 2
12	F	Metaphor	L5.5a	DOK 2
13	B	Context Clues: Sentence Clues	L.5.4a	DOK 2
14	F	Root Words	L.5.4b	DOK 1
15	C	Main Idea and Key Details	RI.5.1	DOK 1
16	I	Cause and Effect	RI.5.3	DOK 2
17	C	Cause and Effect	RI.5.3	DOK 3
18	H	Author's Point of View	RI.5.8	DOK 3
19	B	Idioms	L.5.5b	DOK 2
20	H	Simile	L.5.5a	DOK 2

Copyright © The McGraw-Hill Companies, Inc.

Question	Correct Answer	Content Focus	CCSS	Complexity
21	B	Text Features: Charts	RI.4.7	DOK 2
22	H	Text Features: Charts	RI.4.7	DOK 2
23	D	Synonyms	L.5.5c	DOK 2
24	I	Latin Roots	L.5.4b	DOK 1
25	B	Character, Setting, Plot: Character	RL.5.1	DOK 3
26	H	Character, Setting, Plot: Character	RL.5.3	DOK 3
27	A	Character, Setting, Plot: Compare and Contrast	RL.5.3	DOK 2
28	I	Theme	RL.5.2	DOK 3
29	D	Idioms	L.5.5b	DOK 2
30	H	Simile	L.5.5a	DOK 2
31	D	Character, Setting, Plot: Sequence	RL.3.3	DOK 2
32	F	Character, Setting, Plot: Setting	RL.5.3	DOK 3
33	B	Point of View	RL.6.6	DOK 2
34	G	Point of View	RL.6.6	DOK 3
35	B	Root Words	L.5.4b	DOK 1
36	I	Context Clues: Multiple-Meaning Words	L.5.4a	DOK 2
37	B	Main Idea and Key Details	RI.5.2	DOK 2
38	H	Author's Point of View	RI.5.8	DOK 3
39	A	Main Idea and Key Details	RI.5.2	DOK 3
40	I	Idioms	L.5.5b	DOK 2

Copyright © The McGraw-Hill Companies, Inc.

Part I: Reading Answer Key   Name: _____

Question	Correct Answer	Content Focus	CCSS	Complexity
41	A	Adages	L.5.5b	DOK 2
42	H	Metaphor	L.5.5a	DOK 2
43	C	Text Features: Timelines	RI.4.7	DOK 2
44	I	Text Features: Use Illustrations	RI.4.7	DOK 2
45	D	Context Clues: Paragraph Clues	L.5.4a	DOK 2
46	G	Synonyms	L.5.5c	DOK 2
47	D	Text Structure: Problem and Solution	RI.5.3	DOK 2
48	I	Text Structure: Sequence	RI.5.3	DOK 2
49	D	Cause and Effect	RI.5.3	DOK 2
50	G	Personification	L.5.5a	DOK 2
51	B	Idioms	L.5.5b	DOK 2
52	H	Idioms	L.5.5b	DOK 2
53	A	Text Features: Headings	RI.4.7	DOK 2
54	H	Context Clues: Paragraph Clues	L.5.4a	DOK 2
55	B	Character, Setting, Plot: Character	RL.5.3	DOK 3
56	F	Theme	RL.5.2	DOK 3
57	C	Character, Setting, Plot: Character	RL.5.3	DOK 2
58	G	Point of View	RL.5.6	DOK 3
59	B	Point of View	RL.5.6	DOK 2
60	H	Character, Setting, Plot: Compare and Contrast	RL.5.3	DOK 2

Reporting Category 1 1, 2, 11, 13, 14, 23, 24, 35, 36, 45, 46, 54	/12	%	
Reporting Category 2 3–6, 15–18, 28, 37–39, 47–49, 56	/16	%	
Reporting Category 3 7, 8, 9, 12, 19, 20, 25–27, 29–32, 33, 34, 40–42, 50–52, 55, 57, 58–60	/26	%	
Reporting Category 4 10, 21, 22, 43, 44, 53	/6	%	
Total Reading Score	/60	%	

Copyright © The McGraw-Hill Companies, Inc.

Question	Correct Answer	Content Focus	CCSS	Complexity
1	C	Prewriting: Organizing	W.5.2b	DOK 2
2	G	Prewriting: Organizing	W.5.2b	DOK 2
3	A	Prewriting: Organizing	W.5.2b	DOK 2
4	H	Prewriting: Organizing	W.5.2a	DOK 2
5	D	Subjects and Predicates	L.4.1f	DOK 1
6	G	Nouns in Prepositional Phrases	L.5.1a	DOK 1
7	D	Independent and Dependent Clauses	L.5.2	DOK 1
8	I	Adjectives	L.5.1	DOK 1
9	B	Verb Tenses	L.5.1c	DOK 1
10	F	Pronouns and Antecedents	L.3.1f	DOK 1
11	C	Prepositional Phrases as Adjectives and Adverbs	L.5.1a	DOK 1
12	G	Irregular Verbs	L.5.1c	DOK 1
13	A	Pronouns and Antecedents	L.3.1f	DOK 1
14	H	Main Verbs and Helping Verbs	L.5.1c	DOK 1
15	B	Possessive Pronouns	L.5.2	DOK 1
16	F	Verb Tenses	L.5.1c	DOK 1
17	C	Homophones	L.4.1g	DOK 1
18	G	Subjects and Predicates (Correlative Conjunctions)	L.5.1e	DOK 1
19	B	Compound Sentences and Conjunctions	L.5.1a	DOK 1
20	I	Prepositional Phrases as Adjectives and Adverbs	L.5.1a	DOK 1

Copyright © The McGraw-Hill Companies, Inc.

Part 2: Writing Answer Key

Name: _____

Question	Correct Answer	Content Focus	CCSS	Complexity
21	D	Possessive Pronouns	L.5.2	DOK 1
22	I	Complex Sentences	L.5.1	DOK 2
23	A	Adjectives	L.5.1	DOK 1
24	G	Complex Sentences	L.5.2	DOK 1
25	D	Sentence Combining	L.5.1	DOK 2
26	G	Main Verbs and Helping Verbs	L.5.1b	DOK 1
27	C	Complex Sentences	L.5.1	DOK 1
28	H	Main Verbs and Helping Verbs	L.5.1	DOK 1
29	A	Homophones	L.4.1g	DOK 1
30	F	Verb Tenses	L.5.1c	DOK 1
31	B	Main Verbs and Helping Verbs	L.5.1c	DOK 1
32	H	Verb Tenses	L.5.1c	DOK 1
33	A	Irregular Verbs	L.5.1c	DOK 1
34	G	Possessive Pronouns	L.5.2	DOK 1
35	D	Subjects and Predicates	L.5.1	DOK 1
36	G	Compound Sentences and Conjunctions	L.5.1a	DOK 2
37	B	Subjects and Predicates	L.5.1	DOK 1
38	H	Sentence Combining	L.5.2	DOK 2
39	A	Prepositional Phrases as Adjectives and Adverbs	L.5.1a	DOK 1

Copyright © The McGraw-Hill Companies, Inc.

Part 2: Writing Answer Key

Question	Correct Answer	Content Focus	CCSS	Complexity
40	H	Independent and Dependent Clauses	L.5.2	DOK 1
41	D	Nouns in Prepositional Phrases	L.5.1a	DOK 1
42	I	Complex Sentences	L.5.2	DOK 1
43	B	Complex Sentences	L.5.2	DOK 1
44	F	Main Verbs and Helping Verbs	L.5.1c	DOK 1
45	C	Possessive Pronouns	L.5.1	DOK 1
46	F	Adjectives	L.5.1	DOK 1
47	C	Verb Tenses	L.5.1c	DOK 1
48	H	Irregular Verbs	L.5.1c	DOK 1
49	B	Compound Sentences and Conjunctions	L.5.1e	DOK 1
50	F	Pronouns and Antecedents	L.3.1f	DOK 1
Prompt	See below	Opinion Writing	W.5.1a–d	DOK 3

Prewriting /Organization 1–4	/4	%
English Language Conventions 5–50	/46	%
Total Writing Score	/50	%

Writing Prompt

Refer to scoring criteria in the Teacher Introduction.

Copyright © The McGraw-Hill Companies, Inc.